Excerpts from two of the stories:

From "Danelle and Taz"

Danelle stopped yelling for help and looked over at her dog.

"I'm dying, Taz," she said in a shaky voice. Taz cocked his head and stared deep into Danelle's eyes with a knowing expression.

"Help me, Taz. Do something ... I know you can do something, boy," Danelle said as tears fell down her cheeks. *But he's just a dog,* Danelle thought hopelessly. Even so, Taz cocked his head again as though he understood. Then he disappeared, zigzagging back up the cliffs.

From "The Life Riskers"

"Watch out! Get back to the boat!" Joanie was screaming and waving her hands at me. Rick was just standing there, his face white as a sheet. He was pointing to something h Before I could turn to see was pointing at, I turned to loo alligator wa was literally a was headed direct is mouth was already ope

A Background Note about
Animal Rescue

Every so often, a story about a pet that saves its owner's life will make the front pages of the morning newspaper. We may read the story and find it hard to believe, shaking our heads and wondering if the pet's owner made the whole thing up. After all, most of the animals we've ever known, while loving and devoted, are not exactly heroes.

Even so, animals that risk their lives or use their intelligence to save humans are more common than we know. And the stories are real. In *Animal Rescue*, you will read about some of these brave animal heroes and the amazing things they have done. All of the stories are based on true events. Sometimes names, locations, conversations, and other details have been changed in order to bring the story to life. But the animals' courageous accomplishments are true.

And in several stories in this book, humans return the favor by helping animals. Perhaps it doesn't seem as remarkable to think about people rescuing animals. But showing kindness, selflessness, and love is no less admirable than showing bravery. When we reveal these qualities in our attempts to rescue creatures more helpless than ourselves, we are heroes, too.

Tanya Savory

ANIMAL RESCUE

TP THE TOWNSEND LIBRARY

ANIMAL RESCUE

TP **THE TOWNSEND LIBRARY**

For more titles in the Townsend Library,
visit our website: www.townsendpress.com

Copyright © 2008 by Townsend Press.
Printed in the United States of America.

0 9 8 7 6 5 4 3 2

Illustrations © 2008 by Hal Taylor

All rights reserved. For permission to reproduce any
material in this book, send requests to:

Townsend Press, Inc.
439 Kelley Drive
West Berlin, New Jersey 08091
cs@townsendpress.com

ISBN-13: 978-1-59194-107-1
ISBN-10: 1-59194-107-5

Library of Congress Control Number:
2007910369

CONTENTS

A CHANGE OF HEART

Preview

Some people believe
what they've always
heard: "Cats bring
bad luck." "They're
unfriendly." "They're
afraid of everything."
But in this story we
meet an unusual cat
that is determined to
prove that you can't
believe everything
you hear.

A CHANGE OF HEART

Jen Thompson was waiting at the bus stop one Tuesday morning with her two friends, Jake and Sam, when they saw an old blue pickup truck weaving back and forth across the lanes. It went completely off the road twice and ran right over a mailbox. Still, it kept coming toward the three nine-year-olds.

"Whoa. What's up with *that* driver?" Jen asked.

"I don't know," Jake answered. "Looks like something I saw in a scary movie one time."

"Y'all just gonna stand there?" Sam yelled from behind a fence, way off the road. "I don't wanna die before the bus gets here."

Jen and Jake scurried away from the edge of the road and climbed over the fence just in time. The rusty blue pickup careened along the gravel shoulder of the road and then screeched to a dramatic stop. Dust blew everywhere, and a loud, raspy voice blasted from inside the cab of the pickup.

"Dang it all! You little . . . STOP! Get offa me!! Oh, for the love of . . ."

The door of the truck suddenly hurled open. A very large middle-aged woman swung around to face the three kids. She was wearing huge curlers in her very badly dyed red hair, a pair of work boots, and a bathrobe. Jake and Jen looked at each other and burst into giggles. Sam, however, looked as though he might faint from fear.

"Hey!" the woman bellowed, silencing Jake and Jen mid-giggle. "Listen to me!"

The three children stared at the strange woman who stared back at them fiercely as though she was about to deliver an extremely important message.

"Want a cat?" she finally asked.

"Oh, no, ma'am," Sam answered right away in a shaky voice. "My mama would never allow that. No siree. Why, if I ever just showed up with a cat, I . . ."

"What about you?" the woman thundered, pointing at Jake and pushing a flop of red hair out of her eyes.

Jake just shrugged. "Already got a dog."

"Well, I can't keep this blasted thing," the woman yelled. "It hates me and I hate it. Done given me scratches all upside one arm and down the other."

With that, she lifted a large black cat by the scruff of its neck and held it out in front of her. The cat immediately hissed and swiped at the woman with all ten claws on its front feet fully extended.

"Ow!! Devil cat!" the woman screeched at the cat, who looked both furious and terrified. "Here—he's all yours," she said, flinging the cat in Jen's direction.

With that, the woman heaved herself back around into the driver's seat and slammed the door. The rusty blue truck roared off in a cloud of dust.

The three kids all looked at each other blankly for a moment and then crouched down to look at the cat. He was huddled behind an old rotten log, shaking slightly and growling.

"Come here, kitty. It's all right. Here kitty, kitty." Jen tried to coax the cat out of his hiding place, but he only bushed his tail out and hissed.

"Here comes the bus," Sam announced in an obviously relieved voice. But Jen didn't move.

Jake looked at Jen and shook his head. "Hey, Jen. You have to go to school. They'll call your mom."

"But I can't leave this poor cat alone."

"Jen's gonna get in trouble," Sam said in a sing-song voice as he ran happily to the bus. Jen just ignored Sam and waved quickly to Jake.

"It's okay. I think I'd better stay for just a few more minutes. I'll just tell my mom I missed the bus, and she'll give me a ride. No big deal."

Three hours later, Jen was still on her hands and knees trying to get the black cat to come to her. He had eaten half of the bologna sandwich Jen had packed for lunch. She had set it down in front of him, and he had crept up to take bites. But he only muttered and hissed when she spoke to him or tried to reach out and touch him.

"You're scared, aren't you?" Jen asked softly. "It's a good thing to be scared of strangers, I guess. But you don't have to be scared of me. I'm your friend—I won't hurt you."

Jen was so involved in trying to convince the cat of her friendship that she didn't hear a car pull up.

"Jennifer!" Jen's mother, Sally, got out of the car and slammed the door. "What on earth are you doing? I was scared half out of my mind when the school called to ask why you weren't there today."

"Oh, Mom, I'm sorry. This lady—she threw a cat out and then it was scared and I think it's hungry and . . ."

"Jennifer, calm down. What are you talking about?"

Jen just pointed to the black cat huddled by the half-eaten sandwich. Sally's angry expression melted instantly, and she came over to kneel by her daughter.

"Well, look at you," Sally said gently, looking at the cat.

"Can I keep him, Mom?"

Sally stared at the cat for a minute and sighed. "No, Jen. I wish I could say yes, but you know your father doesn't really like cats. He's always been particularly bothered by black cats. Thinks they bring bad luck."

"But what if the cat follows me home? Can he live outside?"

"Well . . ."

"Oh please, Mom. I know you love cats, too."

Jen's mom looked up the hill to their trailer. It was only about fifty yards away, so there was a good chance that the cat would end up hanging around the trailer anyway. She looked back at the cat. He was fearfully inching forward to sneak another bite of sandwich.

"It's all right with me, but you'll have to ask your father, too, when he gets back on Saturday," Sally finally said. Jen's father, Larry, drove a truck and was often gone for a week or more at a time.

Jen began jumping up and down with excitement. Naturally, this startled the cat and sent him scurrying further into the woods. Jen immediately began following him.

"Oh no you don't," Sally said, grabbing Jen's hand. "You're going to school. You've already missed half the day."

"But the cat . . ." Jen began.

"Look, Jen," Sally said patiently as they got in the car, "as cruel as it is, people dump animals on the side of the road every day. Some survive and some don't. We'll give this little guy a chance if we can, but it's up to him. You can't keep following after him."

Jen stared into the woods and just nodded

as they drove away. She knew her mother was right, but she wondered if she'd ever see the cat again.

After school, Jen rushed up the hill to the trailer and spent an hour calling the black cat. But there was no sign of him. At the dinner table, Jen was on the verge of tears and barely touched her food. Sally tried to take her daughter's mind off the cat, but it was no use. Finally, Sally walked over to the refrigerator and took out a carton of milk.

"All right," Sally said, shaking her head. "We'll put some milk and food on the back step."

For four nights, Jen and her mother left food on the steps, and every morning it had disappeared.

"Do you think it's the cat or just a raccoon eating the food?" Jen asked every day at breakfast. And every day at breakfast, Sally told her daughter she didn't know. But Sally had found a black cat whisker in the empty milk bowl one morning. However, she didn't want to get Jen's hopes up too high.

On the fifth morning, Saturday, Jen ran outside to check the bowls. As before, they were empty, but this time there was a dead mouse lying in the empty food bowl. Jen jumped about a foot, shrieked, and bolted back inside to tell her mother. Sally grinned.

"That's your cat," she said. "He's leaving a little thank-you gift for the food you've been giving him."

"And look," Sally nearly whispered, pointing out the back window. Out in the middle of the backyard was the black cat, stretching in the morning sun and batting at a fly.

Both Jen and her mother tiptoed to the back door and then opened it very slowly. Jen walked just to the edge of the back step and stood very still. She was certain that the cat would scurry away as soon as it saw her. But then something totally unexpected happened—the cat jumped up and trotted right over to Jen, rubbing against her legs and purring. Jen looked over to her mother, a silent question on her face.

"I think your cat has had a change of heart," Sally said.

"What does that mean?" Jen asked, reaching down to gently pet the happy cat.

"Well, " Sally said, thinking for a moment. "It means that something has happened to change his mind. And because of that, it has changed the way he feels—it's changed his heart."

"The food?" Jenny asked. "Did the food change his heart?"

"I'm sure it helped," Sally answered with

a laugh.

Later that afternoon, Larry returned home from his trip. Jen exploded through the back door to meet her father out in the yard, and she nearly knocked him over with hugs and kisses.

"Okay," he said in a dry tone. "What do you want?"

"What makes you think I want anything?" Jen asked casually. "I'm just glad to see you."

"Hmmm. Okay. Well, I'm flattered, then," Larry said with a smile as he hugged Jen.

At that exact moment, as though he were following a script, the black cat came strutting across the yard, plopped himself at Larry's feet, and began a tremendous purring. Larry looked down and then looked at his daughter. Jen was doing her best to appear as though there was absolutely nothing unusual about a strange cat running over to greet her father.

"And I don't suppose *this* has anything to do with how glad you are to see me?"

"Well . . . I . . ."

"Jen, you know that I am not exactly a big fan of cats," Larry said. At that very moment, the black cat looked up at him with huge, loving eyes. Larry sighed.

"Dad, *pleeease*," Jen pleaded. "He's living outside. He catches mice and stuff—he doesn't have anywhere else to go!" Jen's eyes began to fill up with tears.

Larry threw his hands up in the air. "Oh, all right! But he *has* to stay outside. *All* the time. I don't ever want to see even one cat toe inside the front door."

Jen ran over and hugged her father again, saying, "Thank you, thank you, thank you," nonstop. The cat, having completed his performance, wandered back across the yard and sat down to clean his whiskers, totally ignoring Larry.

"You sure are a lucky cat," Larry yelled across the yard. "Especially for being a black cat."

"That's it!" Jen said happily. "*Lucky*. I'm going to name him Lucky."

Within only a couple of weeks, Lucky was managing to put a lot more than just one cat toe inside the door of the trailer. Jen would often sneak Lucky inside when her father was gone and her mother was working late. After all, why should both she and Lucky be lonely? Jen would sit watching TV or reading a book with Lucky curled up in her lap. Then, just before her mother returned home, Jen would gently set Lucky back outside with a few cat treats.

One evening when Jen was alone, she could hear huge thunder claps in the distance. She ran to the door and called for Lucky, not wanting him to be out in the approaching storm. Lucky pranced right into the trailer, happy to be breaking the rules once again. Then Jen sat brushing Lucky and chatting to him as the rain began falling.

Suddenly, Lucky sat up with his ears twitching and his tail growing bushy. His eyes were wide, and he muttered a low warning growl.

"What?" Jen asked, quickly pulling the brush away. "What's wrong?"

At that very moment, there was a loud banging on the front door. The banging went on and on. Every so often, a man's voice would yell, "Hello? Anyone home?" Jen didn't move. She barely breathed, but her heart was beating wildly. *Who would be at the door in the middle of a storm?* she wondered. *And why doesn't he go away if no one's answering the door?* Finally, Jen sneaked to the window and peered out through a slit in the blinds. Banging on the door was a tall man with long, stringy hair. He was wearing a funny-looking uniform of some kind.

"Hello? I know someone's in there!" he shouted between thunderclaps. "I just need to use your phone. My car broke down right out front, and my wife is sick. I need to get her to the hospital. Please help me!"

Jen watched the man for another minute, wondering what to do. She wasn't supposed to open the door to strangers, but maybe she could make the phone call for him. She could just ask him to wait outside while she called. As Jen was figuring out her plan, Lucky paced back and forth by the door, snarling and hissing. Finally, Jen walked over to the door. She made sure the security chain was locked in place, and then she cracked the door open.

"Oh, thank you!" the stranger said, smiling a weird smile that looked more angry than happy. He was missing two front teeth and his hair hung over his eyes. "I just need to come in and . . ."

"I—I can't let you in," Jen stammered. She and the stranger stared at each other through the crack.

"That's okay," he said. "Can you call the hospital for me?"

"Sure." Jen felt relieved that he was not going to continue to ask to come in. She turned to walk over to the phone, leaving the door cracked but chained. Jen had barely picked up the phone to make the call when there was a loud crash. Whirling around, Jen saw that the stranger had thrown himself against the door, breaking the security latch. Before Jen could move, the man had stormed over to her. He grabbed her roughly around the waist and slapped his hand over her mouth.

"You make a sound, you die," the man hissed in her ear. "Scissors. Where are some scissors?" Jen was shaking so badly, she could barely raise her arm. But she managed to point to a drawer. The stranger dragged her to the drawer with him. He pulled out the scissors and then cut the phone lines.

"Now, I need some clothes and some food," he snapped. "I'll find those myself. If you move, I'll kill you." With that, he threw Jen to the floor, kicking her hard in the back as a warning. He stomped to the refrigerator and began pulling out food, throwing things everywhere. Jen waited until the stranger started eating and his back was turned. Then she began to creep toward the back door along the floor.

But just as she reached the door, the man saw her. He rushed over and pulled her to her feet by her hair. Then he slapped her so hard that she fell back over. When she hit the ground, he kicked her again. Crying and gasping for air, Jen reached out blindly to shield herself from the stranger. But he grabbed her hands, trying to pull her to her feet so that he could slap her down again.

It was at this moment that Lucky attacked.

He had been quietly sitting on the top of the refrigerator, and now he lunged down directly on top of the stranger's head. Lucky dug all twenty of his claws into the attacker's skull and bit at his head. The stranger yelled out in pain and anger, trying to pull the cat from his head. But Lucky held on. He raked his claws down the front of the stranger's face and then sank his fangs deep into the man's neck, hissing as he bit and fought.

The stranger had let go of Jen in order to deal with the attack cat. In that split second, Jen tore out the back door of the trailer and ran through the thunderstorm to a neighbor's house just fifty yards away. She was bleeding, and something felt broken on her side near her back. When the shocked neighbor opened the door for Jen, Jen fell to the floor, gasping a few words.

"Help . . . stranger attacked . . . Lucky," Jen barely uttered before she fell to the floor unconscious.

Two days later, news of the heroic cat that had risked his life for his owner was in all the local papers and even on TV. Jen and Lucky sat curled up together on the couch, both of them in bandages for broken ribs. Lucky also had a broken paw. The attacker had been scared off by Lucky's ferocity, but he had hurled the cat against the wall on his way out the door.

"Yep, that cat can stay inside all he wants," Jen's father said with a grin. "Nothing better than the sight of a happy cat in your own home."

Larry had arrived home the day after the incident and was shocked to hear about the escaped prisoner who had broken into their trailer and injured his daughter. The police had caught the fugitive only half a mile away. He was covered in scratches and was unable to see out of one eye.

"Thought you didn't like cats," Sally said to her husband as she winked at Jen.

All that next week, people dropped by the trailer to bring well wishes and gifts to Jen and her hero cat, Lucky. Often, Jen didn't even know the people who came by. One afternoon, a strange woman in a baseball cap knocked on the door. Jen came to the door holding Lucky.

"Well, he sure is a good cat, isn't he?" the woman said. She reached in her purse and pulled out a check for $200.

"Just something to help with his vet bills. Maybe buy him a special treat, too." The woman then tried to pet Lucky, but Lucky let out a quiet growl. The woman just smiled and turned to leave.

Two hundred dollars! Jen could hardly believe anyone could be so generous. She watched the woman walk away. *Why do I feel like I know her?* Jen wondered to herself. When the woman reached the road, she pulled off the baseball cap. Poorly dyed red hair fell to her shoulders. Then the woman climbed inside a rusty blue pickup truck and drove away. Jen stared open-mouthed. She pulled Lucky close and whispered something in his ear.

"Change of heart," Jen explained to Lucky.

DANELLE AND TAZ

Preview

Danelle loved her dog, Taz, but he didn't seem very smart. One morning, as she went for a run along a steep cliff, something went terribly wrong. Hours later, badly hurt and bleeding, Danelle looked at Taz and whispered, "Help me." But how could Taz understand?

DANELLE AND TAZ

"**N**o, Taz! No!" Danelle was standing at her back door yelling at her puppy, Taz, who was once again trying to jump over a little fence in the backyard. Next door was the home of an elderly widow, Dorothy. Taz had discovered that if he scratched on her back door long enough, Dorothy would appear with two dog biscuits.

"Oh, it's all right, Danelle," Dorothy waved and smiled as she bent down slowly to scratch the brown-and-yellow puppy's head.

"I am so sorry," Danelle said as she opened the gate to her neighbor's yard. "He is a cute thing, but I'm afraid he's not too smart."

"Smart enough to know where he can get a free snack," Dorothy said with a wink as she handed Taz a biscuit.

Danelle smiled, but she worried that her dog would never learn to obey. She had adopted him from an animal shelter when he was only a few weeks old. He was just a stray mutt puppy that had either been abandoned or lost. But Danelle saw something special in him. He was certainly not the most handsome puppy in the shelter. But he seemed to look right at Danelle as if he understood her. And even now, as he was misbehaving, his big golden eyes searched Danelle's face as if to say, "Don't be mad. I'll make it up to you some day."

Danelle picked up Taz and headed back across the yard. Then she stopped and turned back to Dorothy.

"I meant to tell you that I'm going to be gone to Colorado to do the Pike's Peak Marathon next week. Taz will be with some friends . . . just in case you're wondering where we both are."

Dorothy just smiled and nodded. She knew

that her young neighbor was something called an "adventure athlete"—a person who seemed to enjoy running, biking, and hiking races of 20, 40, and even 100 miles across mountains, deserts, and twisting trails. Sometimes Dorothy would see Danelle leaving for a training run at 6:00 in the morning. Many hours later, Dorothy would spy through her window to see Danelle returning, covered in dirt and sweat, looking exhausted but happy. Dorothy thought it seemed like a strange sort of profession. Plus, it sounded very dangerous.

"When's Taz gonna be big enough to run with you?" Dorothy asked before Danelle closed the gate.

Danelle looked doubtfully at the squirming puppy in her arms. "Well, if he's smart enough to figure out that he's supposed to stay with me on a run, he should be big enough in about six months," she answered.

"Bet you'll feel safer then, huh?"

Danelle set Taz down, and he immediately scampered over to the fence again, Danelle chasing behind him.

"Don't know about safer—probably more tired," Danelle said with a sigh.

But within a year and a half, Taz had become a wonderful running companion. Danelle was still not sure how bright he was, but Taz loved the red dirt trails that wound throughout Moab, Utah. He was not afraid of the steep cliffs that Danelle often climbed. And he never whined when he had to run in freezing snow or pouring rain.

Taz had grown into a big, strong dog—some sort of German shepherd and Labrador mix with a few other things thrown in. He was able to keep up with his athletic master no matter how long or hilly the trail turned out to be. However, again and again Taz would keep running even after Danelle stopped. Danelle would shout after him, and eventually Taz would stop, turn around, and tilt his head to one side, staring hard at his owner. Then he would bound away several yards, turn back around, and tilt his head again at Danelle.

"No, I am not following you! The run is over!" Danelle would call after Taz with a weary grin. Then Taz would leap playfully back to his master and nuzzle her. Danelle would lean over to give Taz a big hug.

"You crazy, stupid dog," she would whisper affectionately as she patted his neck.

One chilly December morning, two weeks before Christmas, Danelle rattled her car keys—the signal to Taz that it was time for a run. As the two piled into her pickup truck, Danelle looked at her watch and frowned. She needed to run ten miles that morning, but there wasn't enough time. Christmas shopping and coaching duties were going to take up much of the day.

As she drove to a remote trail five miles outside of Moab, Danelle thought about how she could cut a few miles off the run. She would have to go off the trail and take a short-cut around some steep cliffs. She had done it a couple of times last summer. It was no big deal. Plus, the sharp climb around the cliffs would be great practice for the upcoming race in January.

"Ready for a tough one?" she asked Taz as they pulled into the small lot by the trail. Taz looked at Danelle briefly and licked her hand and whined a little. He was always impatient to get going. He couldn't under-stand why Danelle spent so much time fiddling with things before they started running, and this morning was no exception. Danelle put on a warm hat and a pair of orange sunglasses. Then she put on a light fleece jacket, making sure there were a couple of energy snacks in the pockets. Finally, she filled a water bottle and slipped it into a lightweight pack that she wore around her waist. The run would take only about an hour and a half, but Danelle always wanted to be prepared. All the while, Taz paced in circles, sniffed the air, and sighed loudly.

Finally, they were off. Taz seemed to be grinning from ear to ear as he trotted easily behind Danelle. And it really was a beautiful day—a dim December sun shone off the red rocks of the canyons and the air smelled of pine. More than once, Danelle spotted eagles flying high above. About five miles into the run, Danelle found the spot where she would cut through the cliffs.

"Come on, Taz!" Danelle shouted. Taz had continued along the trail like always. He stopped and looked confused. He sat down on the trail.

"Taz!" Danelle yelled again, irritated that she had to stop. Finally, Taz reluctantly followed his owner. But first he stopped to sniff the edge of the trail and gaze back in the direction they had come from.

"Darn it! Come *on*!" Danelle took off quickly. Taz loped behind her, glancing back a couple of times at the trail. They ran up a very steep hill, and suddenly they were running along the edge of a series of cliffs. But then something happened. It was something that Taz could not understand at all. One minute, his master had been running along in front of him, but the next she had disappeared. Taz had heard a scream, some gravel falling far below, a small thud, and then silence.

Taz trotted back and forth along the ledge. He looked up and sniffed the air, whining quietly. *What had happened?* Then he looked down. Nearly sixty feet down in the canyon, Danelle lay motionless. She had slipped on a small patch of ice and fallen off the cliff and into the canyon, bouncing off two cliff edges on her way down. Amazingly, she had landed on her feet. But the impact had been so forceful that she had shattered her hip in three places and cracked two vertebrae.

Taz surveyed the cliffs quickly. Then he zigzagged his way down to Danelle, dashing to her side and immediately licking her face. She opened her eyes and tried to sit up, but the pain slammed through her body, keeping her down.

"Taz, I'm hurt," Danelle whispered. Taz wagged his tail and stared at her with his piercing gold eyes. Why didn't she get up? Wasn't it time to be back at the truck for a snack?

For the rest of that morning and most of the afternoon, Danelle tried to drag herself away from the cliff and closer to another trail she knew of. It was agonizing work pulling herself along with her arms, but she knew that she might not make it through the night when the temperatures would fall into the 20s or teens. She *had* to get near a trail where some-one might hear or see her. But after hours of work, Danelle had barely moved a quarter mile. Finally, she gave up. She ate one of her energy snacks and drank a little water. Taz, who had been closely watching his master with a worried expression, came over and stretched out beside Danelle. Then he rested his long muzzle on her chest and gazed at her calmly as the sun began sinking in the western sky.

Danelle fell in and out of consciousness. She was vaguely aware of the fact that Taz kept disappearing for an hour or so and then returning to lick her face and rest next to her. But when the night finally fell, Taz did not leave again. In fact, he crawled gently on top of Danelle and spread himself out over her to keep her warm—something Danelle had never seen him do before. Danelle lay very still, watching dozens of shooting stars in the Utah sky and listening to Taz's light snoring.

"Good boy, Taz," she said quietly before falling asleep.

The next morning, Taz was up and playing with a stick. The sun was shining on Danelle, warming her up, but she knew something was terribly wrong. A lump the size of a grapefruit was swelling around her waist. Danelle knew she was bleeding internally. If someone didn't find her soon, she would die. Danelle began calling and screaming for help over and over again, praying that someone somewhere would hear her. Taz dropped his stick and stared at his master in fear. His ears flattened and his tail drooped between his legs. He sat down, watching Danelle.

Danelle stopped yelling and looked over at her dog.

"I'm dying, Taz," she said in a shaky voice. Taz cocked his head and stared deep into Danelle's eyes with a knowing expression.

"Help me, Taz. Do something . . . I know you can do something, boy," Danelle said as tears fell down her cheeks. *But he's just a dog*, Danelle thought hopelessly. Even so, Taz cocked his head again as though he understood. Then he disappeared, zigzagging back up the cliffs.

Back in Moab, Dorothy was beginning to worry about her young neighbor. It was not like Danelle to leave overnight without saying anything about it. Plus, her lights had stayed on all night. And Dorothy could see Danelle's computer sitting on the kitchen table—it had been on all night, too. Dorothy watched the clock, wanting to call Danelle's parents in Colorado. *But maybe I'm just being a nosy old fool*, Dorothy thought. *I should mind my own business.*

But by 4:00 that afternoon, Dorothy no longer cared if people thought she was nosy. She contacted Danelle's parents.

"Something's wrong," Dorothy explained. "I'm afraid something's happened to Danelle."

It was too late in the day for the Moab

Search and Rescue Team to begin looking for Danelle, but they promised her parents that they would be out first thing in the morning.

"Don't worry," John Marshall, the head of the team, reassured Danelle's parents. "We'll find her. She'll be fine."

But John wasn't so sure. Just a few weeks earlier, two hunters had gotten lost and had frozen to death after two nights. They were bigger and had been wearing heavy hunting jackets and vests—not just running clothes. John sighed and looked at his watch: 7:30 p.m. If Danelle was still alive, it was going to be a long and very cold night.

"What? What? . . . Hello?" Danelle turned her head back and forth, staring up into the 3 a.m. sky. She was beginning to hear voices and see odd streaks of light. For hours, she had been trying to keep her fingers and feet moving so that they wouldn't get frostbite. But, slowly, she was beginning to give up and accept that she was going to die right there in that canyon. She stopped wiggling her toes. She closed her eyes.

Keep moving. A voice seemed to speak to her. Her eyes flew open just as a flash of strange light burst through the sky.

"Who's there? Help me!" Danelle said in a weak, hoarse voice. *I'm beginning to lose my mind*, Danelle thought. *My body is finally shutting down. This is it.*

Several feet away from her, Taz sat watching. He had refused to come near her since the afternoon, and Danelle knew why. She had often heard that a dog can smell death and will not touch a dying animal. Now, she was that dying animal. Still, Taz guarded his master faithfully, resting his head on his paws and fixing his gaze on Danelle all night.

Danelle forced herself to keep moving, to stay awake, to fight. Surely someone had noticed her missing by now. If she could just hold on until daylight . . . Danelle ate the second energy snack and finished the last of her water. She counted to 100. She thought hard about all the people she loved. *I am not ready to die*, she thought fiercely. *Not yet*. Then Danelle thought about some of the toughest races she had endured: a 3-day race through a brutal desert, a 31-mile run up and down the tallest mountain in Vermont, a marathon on snowshoes. *I will make it through this, too*, she vowed to herself.

With the first rays of sunlight, Taz stood up, came as near to Danelle as he dared, and sniffed her. He stared at her for a moment and then ran away fast.

"Taz!" Danelle tried to shout, but only a whispered rasp came out. She did not want to be alone. Although the voices and streaks of light had stopped, Danelle knew that she would not make it through another night. If no one found her today, these would be her last hours. She wanted and needed the comfort of Taz's presence.

Two hours later, John Marshall's team was spread out all through the area where they thought Danelle might be. They had found her truck—a bad sign. Now they knew that she was, in fact, out in the freezing wilderness alone. But where? The team members knew that Danelle often went out for 15–30 mile runs and hikes. That meant a lot of ground to cover—an impossible amount of ground to cover in just ten hours of sunlight.

One of the searchers, a gruff, no-nonsense man named Bego, turned his ATV down a rarely-traveled road. About a half a mile down the road, Bego saw a second very bad sign. Just ahead of him was a big brown and yellow dog that matched the description of Danelle's dog. In the hundreds of rescues Bego had done, he knew that a dog would rarely leave his master unless his master was dead.

Bego called to Taz. Taz backed away. Bego jumped off the ATV and started moving slowly toward Taz, coaxing him quietly. Taz stopped and cocked his head to the side and let Bego get within a few feet of him. Then Taz turned and ran ahead about ten yards. He repeated this same series of movements several times, always watching Bego with a strange intensity and never letting him get too close.

Bego finally stopped. Taz responded by barking loudly and running in circles until Bego began to follow him again. Quickly, Bego got on his radio.

"I'm on Kane Creek Road," Bego reported to the team. "I've found the dog and I know this is gonna sound crazy, but . . ." Here Bego paused to think about just how crazy it was going to sound. "But I think the dog is trying to get me to follow him. If any of you are up ahead, *do not* try and capture the dog. I repeat—leave the dog alone and let him lead the way."

With that, Bego raced back to his ATV and zoomed ahead up to where Taz was waiting. Taz barked excitedly and took off down the road as fast as his four legs could carry him, spinning around every so often to make sure Bego was behind him. Further and further into a very desolate area, the two raced along. Suddenly, Taz stopped and looked at Bego with his bright golden eyes. He barked once and then disappeared down a very steep hill, crisscrossing and looking back up at Bego the entire way.

Then Bego lost sight of Taz. He wasn't able to follow Taz on the ATV, so he ran out to a cliff ledge to get a better view. What Bego saw then was something he would never forget. There—about sixty feet below—lay Danelle. And lying next to her with his head on her chest was Taz. As Taz looked up and barked, Bego saw Danelle lift her hand to stroke Taz's head. *Well, I'll be damned,* Bego thought as he scurried down the hill with blankets and water. *He knew exactly what he was doing. That is one smart dog!*

"I've got her!" Bego shouted over the radio. "She's still alive, but barely. Her dog led me right to her—He's . . . he's saved her life."

A week later, Danelle rested in her hospital bed. A six-hour operation had replaced her shattered hip with a metal plate, and both her feet and hands were wrapped in layers of protective covering for frostbite. She had lost nearly a third of her blood and had suffered both shock and severe dehydration. Still, the doctors told her she would be fine in time, even able to run and possibly compete again.

"But how's Taz?" Danelle would ask again and again, sometimes only half-awake from all the pain medication.

After rescuing Danelle, John and the team had surveyed the area where Danelle had fallen. They were able to trace the exact route she had taken off the trail—it was covered in hundreds of paw prints that led back to her truck, out to the road, down numerous paths. Every time Taz had left Danelle, he'd been out looking for help. Bego was right; Taz had known what he was doing all along.

Just before Christmas, the hospital made an unusual exception to their strict rules. They allowed a visitor after hours—a four-legged visitor with a long snout and bright gold eyes. It was the first time Taz and Danelle had seen each other since her rescue. Taz rushed over to Danelle, his entire body swaying from his tail wagging. Then he gently licked her hand and rested his head on the edge of Danelle's bed.

"I'll bet he gets a couple of extra bones in his stocking this year," one of the nurses said with a smile.

"More like a couple of extra steaks," Danelle joked. Then she stroked Taz's head and quietly said, "You have no idea how important you are."

At that, Taz lifted his head and looked directly into Danelle's eyes.

"Or maybe," Danelle said even more quietly, "you know exactly how important you are."

UNLIKELY HEROES

Preview

When Lassie attacked
a bear in order to save
her owner, it made for
a great TV show. But
what about the less
glamorous heroes? Who
says that a pig can't save
the day? The unusual
stars here may not get
their own TV shows,
but they're heroes, too.

UNLIKELY HEROES

Everyone expects heroic actions from a dog. After all, dogs *are* man's (and woman's) best friends. Dogs lead the blind, help firefighters, sniff out bombs and drugs, and guard homes. But what about other pets? Many of them feel just as much love and devotion for humans as dogs do. True, you may never hear of a hamster rescuing a child from a burning building, but given an emergency situation, even a cat (or a pig or a parrot) will rise to the occasion.

Here are three true stories about these unlikely heroes:

Lulu

"But she's a pig," Jo Ann Altsman said to her daughter, Jackie. Jackie was holding out a four-pound little piglet for her mother to hold.

"Well, obviously," Jackie said. "But pigs are affectionate and smart." Jackie saw her mother's doubtful expression and added, "And very clean."

Jo Ann carefully took the pig from her daughter and held it at arm's length. The pig and Jo Ann stared at each other for a long minute.

"I only need you to take her for a week while I'm out of town," Jackie assured her mother. "She's really not much trouble. Please?"

Jo Ann set the little pig down on her kitchen floor and sighed. "All right. But only for a week. I'm not used to seeing a pig sleeping in my living room."

Two months later, the pig, named Lulu, was still sleeping in Jo Ann's living room. Something always seemed to keep coming up that prevented Jackie from taking her back. At first, Jo Ann and her husband, Jack, were not exactly thrilled with having a pot-bellied pig waddling around their house. Even less thrilled was the family dog, Bear, who could never quite figure out if Lulu was a giant cat or just an ugly dog.

But in time, Jo Ann and Jack became quite fond of Lulu. She was friendly and well behaved. She was actually cleaner than their dog, and she was very cute in her own piggish way. Jo Ann and Lulu, in particular, formed a special bond. Lulu grew from a four-pound piglet to a 200-pound porker, thanks, in part, to the occasional jelly doughnuts that Jo Ann gave her as a special treat.

One beautiful fall day, Jo Ann and Jack decided to take their trailer up to the lake for the weekend so that Jack could do some fishing. As always, they took Lulu and Bear along. After getting the trailer set up and in order, Jack took off with his rod and reel. Jo Ann was just sitting down with a book and a cup of coffee when a terrible feeling overtook her. A tightness in her arm began to spread to her chest. It was the same feeling she had experienced a few years earlier—she knew she was having another heart attack.

"Help! Help!" Jo Ann was able to break a window on the trailer before she fell to the floor. She yelled for help a few times, but no one heard her—except Lulu. She waddled over and stared at Jo Ann's face for several minutes. Lulu made crying sounds, and Jo Ann actually saw some big tears splash down the pig's face. Then Lulu dashed (as fast as a pig can dash) to the doggie door Jack had installed for both the dog and Lulu. But Lulu had gotten so big that she got stuck in the door. Halfway in and halfway out, Lulu wriggled and grunted and snorted until she finally popped through to the outside.

Immediately, Lulu made a waddling bee-line for the busy road just across a small field. When Lulu reached the road, she walked to the middle of it and plopped herself right down on it, effectively blocking an entire lane. A couple of cars slowed down to take a look at what appeared to be a pig taking a nap (talk about hogging the road!), but no one stopped. So Lulu tried a different technique. She stood by the side of the road, and when she saw a car approaching, she deliberately walked out into the road and stared down the driver. Finally, a man pulled his car to the shoulder and stopped.

"What is it, girl?" the man asked, feeling a little foolish as he got out of his car in order to speak to a pig. But Lulu had her answer ready. With a loud squeal, she took off across the field toward the trailer as the man followed behind. Upon reaching the trailer, Lulu wiggled and snorted her way back through the doggie-piggy door again.

"Hello? Anybody home? I think your pig

is distressed!" the man hollered through the screen door.

"The pig's fine," a woman's frantic voice came back. "*I'm* distressed. Please call an ambulance!"

Lulu trotted over and stayed by Jo Ann's side until the ambulance arrived. She closely watched the paramedics strap Jo Ann to a stretcher, adding commentary through snorts and grunts and tears the entire time. She even tried to climb into the back of the ambulance, but the paramedics gently told her "no."

"Your friend will be just fine," they assured Lulu as they patted her gently and placed her back in the trailer.

A week later, Jo Ann sat at home with one hand scratching Lulu's chin and the other constantly picking up the ringing phone. Lulu had become an instant celebrity. Everyone wanted her—*Oprah, David Letterman, The Today Show,* and *National Geographic's Amazing Animals.* Even *Unsolved Mysteries* called. The man who had followed Lulu to the trailer and called the ambulance was never identified, and the show wanted to offer a reward.

Jo Ann hung up the phone and looked at Lulu with a smile. "What's it like to be the world's first heroic hog?"

Lulu just yawned and stared very hard at a paper bag on the table.

"I guess you think you must deserve some kind of special recognition for your achievement, right?"

Lulu snorted and sighed in agreement.

"Okay. Job well done, Lulu," Jo Ann said as she pulled out two jelly doughnuts from the paper bag.

Brando

"Isn't the whole point of owning a parrot the fact that they can talk?" Jim asked his wife, Cindy, as he glared at their brightly colored macaw.

"I read somewhere that they have to be inspired to talk. Show some emotion. You must not be inspiring him," Cindy responded from behind a newspaper. She was not as concerned as her husband was about getting their bird, Brando, to speak.

"Hello! Hello! Hello!" Jim repeated over and over again in a poor imitation of what a parrot's speaking voice might sound like. Brando sat very still and stared steadily at Jim. Now and then, Brando would cock his head to one side as though trying to figure out what on earth was wrong with his owner.

"Polly wanna cracker? Polly wanna cracker?" Jim tried a new approach.

"Oh, for heaven's sake, Jim. At least try to teach him something unusual," Cindy said, peering over the top of the paper.

"Well, I'd be happy to hear him say even one word. I don't think he . . ."

"Screeeeeee! Squaaaawwk!" Brando ruffled his feathers and burst forth with several ear-splitting screeches.

Jim jumped about a foot. "You crazy bird! See? You *do* have a voice," Jim said. "Now all you have to do is turn that hideous noise into some words."

"Squawk," Brando replied indifferently. Then he leaned over backward to preen his tail feathers.

About a week later, Jim came home one evening to a strange sight. Cindy was standing in front of Brando's cage with her hands on her hips and a puzzled look on her face. When Jim walked over to her, she motioned for Jim to be quiet. Then she leaned close to Brando's cage and quietly said, "What?"

"Help me! Please, someone help me!" Brando announced matter-of-factly before hopping down to eat a piece of apple on the bottom of his cage.

"You're kidding!" Jim said, staring at the macaw. "He doesn't utter a word all week, and now his first words are a plea for someone to come and rescue him from us?"

"Please! Oh please, help!" Brando repeated as he munched away and stared calmly at Jim.

Jim rolled his eyes and walked away, muttering, "Idiot bird."

But Cindy had different thoughts. "Wait a minute, Jim. Think about it—here we have a parrot that has never said a word. No one tried to teach him anything before we got him. But now, out of the blue, he has learned several words while we were gone today. How can that have possibly happened?"

Jim sat down in the easy chair across from Brando and stared tiredly at him. "I don't know. Has he been watching action movies while we've been at work?"

"Jim. Be serious. I just can't figure out how . . . do you think he's heard someone calling for help? " Cindy stopped speaking and sat very still, straining her ears. Then she opened a window, listening carefully for several minutes. Suddenly, she looked at Jim. "Do you hear that?"

Jim listened. There was nothing but silence for a minute or so. But then, very faintly in the distance, a voice crying out for help drifted through the open window. Immediately, Brando bellowed an echo: "Help! Help!"

With that, both Jim and Cindy jumped up and ran outside, trying to figure out where the voice was coming from. The evening traffic in front of their apartment kept drowning out the voice, but Jim seemed to think it was coming from across the street behind some old warehouses.

"Call 911," Jim said as he ran back inside to grab a flashlight.

As soon as Jim began walking around the warehouses and shining the flashlight, he heard a desperate voice cry out, "I'm over here! Help me, please . . . over here." Jim followed the voice. Suddenly, the beam of his flashlight shone upon an elderly man trapped against the side of a building by a delivery van.

"Oh, thank you, thank you," the old man was saying over and over again. Jim could tell he was badly hurt, and there was quite a bit of blood on the ground.

"Take it easy now," Jim said. "An ambulance is on the way."

Amazingly, the 70-year-old man, Edward, had been trapped against the wall all day with two broken legs and several crushed ribs. He had been walking over to the back entrance of a warehouse to pick up some plumbing supplies when his van slipped out of "park." It quickly rolled down the hill it was parked on and pinned Edward against the warehouse wall, crushing several bones in the process.

Edward had spent most of the day calling and calling for help. But the busy road had blocked out his voice, and no one inside the warehouse could hear him. As the hours ticked by, Edward had grown weaker and weaker, falling unconscious more than a few times. *No one can hear my voice,* he had realized as the sun began to set. *I'll never live through the night.*

But his voice *had* been heard. All day long, Brando's highly tuned sense of hearing had been picking up the same urgent words and phrases, repeated over and over again. Brando had listened carefully. He had tentatively tried out a few words. By the end of the day, he had mastered his first sentences.

The next evening, Jim sat down across from Brando.

"So, learn any more lifesaving phrases today?" he asked. Brando ignored Jim, choosing instead to gaze admiringly at himself in a mirror that hung from the top of his cage.

"Pretty full of yourself, aren't you?" Jim said with a grin. He watched the parrot for a long time. Finally, Brando grew tried of worshiping himself, and turned to look at Jim.

"Hello! Hello!" Jim tried again, more hopeful this time around. But Brando remained stonily silent.

After several more tries, Jim shrugged his shoulders. "Still not enough emotion for you?" he asked. "Not feeling inspired?"

"Help me," Brando said wearily and tucked his head under his wing for a nap.

Molly and Minnie

In 1992, Carol Smith was taking a walk on a cool, rainy October evening when she saw what looked like two small, scruffy rats scurrying across the street. But when the animals reached the other side of the street, they sat huddled together, staring back at Carol. These were definitely *not* rats.

Carol tiptoed carefully over to the little creatures. As she grew closer, she was heartbroken to realize that they were two very dirty, starving, and soaked kittens. The kittens seemed torn between running away from Carol and crying for her to help them. In their confusion, they did a little of both—running up to Carol and mewing pitifully, and then bolting away.

Carol was able to finally pick up both kittens. She tucked them into the big warm pocket of her wool coat and hurried home. Once back, she dried the kittens and gently placed them on old blankets near a heater. She set two bowls of milk and tuna out for the kittens. Then she watched them until nearly midnight. Both looked as though they had been separated from their mother at too young an age. One could barely walk without collapsing, and the other one mostly sat still, shaking and crying.

For the next few days, Carol worked tirelessly to save the little kittens' lives. She took them to the vet and received a special formula that she had to feed to them through an eye-dropper. She held them and spoke softly to them until they slept. And she allowed them to sleep on her own bed.

A month later, Carol found herself with two furry bullets of energy and affection. Both kittens dashed down the stairs to meet her every evening, playing around her feet, and purring tremendously the entire time. It was hard for Carol to imagine that these were the same two pathetic strays she had found only four weeks earlier. Carol had decided to name them "Molly" and "Minnie." Both kittens were well behaved and gentle. However, when they were about four months old, something strange began happening.

"What . . . what?" Carol awoke from a dead sleep once again to find Molly pawing her face and tickling her with her whiskers.

"Molly, no!" Carol sat up and moved the kitten to the foot of the bed. But as she fell back to sleep, she could feel Molly quietly creeping up near her head again. Molly would then rest very close to Carol, keeping her eyes half open and watching. *But for what?* Carol would wonder as she drifted back to sleep. It was not unusual for Molly to tap Carol awake two or three times a night. This went on for a few months, and no matter what Carol tried, she could not break Molly's new habit.

Then one day at a routine checkup, Carol happened to mention how tired she had been.

"Of course," Carol said with a laugh, "it doesn't help having a kitten that insists on waking you up two or three times a night."

The doctor smiled, but she also asked a few more questions which led to a couple of tests which led to a discovery—Carol had a dangerous condition that made her stop breathing at times while she was sleeping.

"Let me ask you this, " the doctor said thoughtfully. "Do you ever feel out of breath or dizzy when your cat wakes you up?"

Carol looked surprised. "Well, yes, almost always. But I just thought it was because the cat startles me."

"I can't be certain of it," the doctor replied, "but I think your cat is tapping you awake when you stop breathing. I'd be interested to know if she stops tapping you when you start taking medication that regulates your breathing."

Within two nights of taking the medicine, Molly's tapping ceased. She still slept by Carol's head for a couple of weeks, but eventually she moved back to her old spot at the foot of the bed by Minnie.

A year later, Carol was again being

awakened—this time by Minnie. However, Minnie chose to wake Carol up by walking up and down her body and then sitting on her chest and meowing loudly. Carol paid close attention to how she felt when she woke up. She felt fine; plus, she was still taking medication. Obviously, Minnie was just going through an annoying cat phase. Carol ignored Minnie even though she was not too happy to be awakened nearly every night.

But then one evening while on her walk, Carol became very dizzy and her heart began racing and skipping beats. Carol woke up in the hospital emergency room, hooked up to a heart monitor. All that night and the next, nurses came in to wake Carol up whenever her heart began beating too rapidly or stopped beating for more than a few seconds. Suddenly, it dawned on Carol that this was exactly what Minnie had been doing for nearly a month.

An operation and a few years later, Carol no longer had breathing or heart problems. Neither Minnie nor Molly ever woke her up at night again. Carol would often look with amazement at the two cats whose lives she had saved all those years ago.

"Thanks for returning the favor," Carol would say to both cats nearly every night before turning out the light.

THE LIFE RISKERS

Preview

What if a snake three times your size suddenly attacked your best friend—would you think twice before grabbing hold of it and trying to pull it off? Meet three animals whose love and fearlessness take over when there's no time to think twice.

THE LIFE RISKERS

Some pets are happy to spend all of their time sleeping and eating. Sprawled out on sofas or in backyards, these animals don't really seem to have too many goals. They just want to be comfortable. But then there are animals that are eager to protect a house, work on a farm, or provide companionship. They are willing to work hard day after day to give their owners what is expected from them.

But beyond this are the animals that give

far more than what could ever be expected. These animals are fearless and will walk straight into deadly danger. Without a second thought, they are willing to risk their own lives for the humans they love.

• • •

I'm lucky to be alive.

It was just another fun day out on the lake like a hundred other times before. My friends, Joanie and Rick, met me at the dock with a couple of coolers and their old dog, Poochie. Poochie is a crazy mutt. She has one brown eye and one blue eye—something that always kind of freaks me out. She also has only about three teeth left due to some kind of gum disease. I can't count how many times I've told Rick that he needs to give that dog some mouthwash. To top it off, Poochie can't bark. She just opens her mouth and lets out a hissing sort of sputter.

Even so, I've always loved that dog. I'll admit it. Whenever she comes out to the lake with us, I throw her ball in the water so many times that my shoulder is sore for a week. That dog is supposed to be about 85 in human years, so I have no idea where she gets the energy to swim out in the lake to retrieve her ball over and over again. But it's impossible to stop throwing it once you've started—she gets a look on her face that kills me. How can I tell her "no"?

Anyway, after meeting at the dock, we all went out on the lake in Rick's boat. The lake is a small one down in southern Florida, not too far from the Everglades. It has its share of giant mosquitoes and snapping turtles, but nothing too scary has ever lurked around in this lake. Until last week, that is.

I had thrown Poochie's ball out into the middle of the lake for about the thirtieth time when I decided to take a little swim myself. It must have been over 100 degrees that day. I jumped in and swam out to where Poochie was paddling around. She loves to have anyone in the water with her, so she began her sputtering noises right away. But then she suddenly stopped. It was strange—I felt the little prickly hairs on the back of my neck stand up. Then everything seemed to move in slow motion.

"Watch out! Quick . . . get back to the boat!" Joanie was screaming and waving her hands at me. Rick was just standing there, his face white as a sheet. He was pointing to something behind me. Before I could turn to see what Rick was pointing at, I heard it. It sounded just like a boat cutting through water. It was that big. When I turned to look, my blood froze. A huge alligator was moving so quickly that it was literally above the water. And it was headed directly toward me! Its mouth was already open, and I could see hundreds of razor-sharp teeth glistening.

I turned to frantically swim back to the boat, but I could hear the gator gaining on me. That's when I heard a loud hissing and sputtering above all the other racket. And suddenly, the swishing noise of the approaching gator stopped. Poochie had positioned herself between me and the gator, and she was doing her best to scare it by "barking" as loudly as she could. Her ball was drifting toward the gator's big mouth—something that seemed to confuse it.

I took advantage of that split second that the gator lost interest in me to swim like a crazed man back to the boat. Rick and Joanie pulled me to safety just as we heard a loud *snap* and a splash. The three of us stared out to the water in horror—Poochie was nowhere to be seen. Her ball bobbed on the rippling water, but both she and the alligator were gone.

"Poochie!" Joanie screamed. Rick covered his eyes as though he couldn't bear to see what might happen next. I whipped around to look behind us and in every direction. But there was no trace of the old dog.

Then a faint hissing drifted up from near the front of the boat. We all dashed toward the sound, and there, with her head barely above the water, was poor Poochie. Blood was pouring from one of her legs, but she was still alive. Rick reached down and quickly grabbed her. Strangely, the gator had disappeared for good—apparently it didn't care for the taste of old dog. But in its attempt to get that taste, the gator had bitten off a big part of Poochie's left hind leg.

The good news is that Poochie lived. We rushed her to an animal hospital, and they took great care of her until Rick and Joanie were able to bring her home, minus one leg. I went over to visit her right away with a couple of "get well" presents: some doggie treats and a stuffed alligator toy for her to chew on.

We still all go out on Rick's boat, but we go to a different, safer lake now. As you might imagine, Poochie can no longer chase balls out into the water. But she's discovered something else that's just as fun. Now she likes to push her ball with her nose until it goes over the side of the boat and into the water. Then, I have to dive in and retrieve it for her. She's been known to make me do this two dozen times in one day. But I don't really mind. After all—she saved my life.

• • •

In 1930, a storm blew in across the Pacific Ocean and hit the waters near Seattle, Washington. Two men, Arthur Clayton and Charlie Coulson, were out on a tugboat about a quarter mile from the shore when, suddenly, the waves began growing as tall as houses.

"Arthur! Send an S.O.S!" Charlie shouted above the scream of the wind.

"Won't make any difference," Arthur yelled back. "No one will be able to get a boat out to us in time!"

Even so, Arthur sent several S.O.S. signals just in case. But in his heart, he knew that he and Charlie were doomed. Deep inside, Arthur knew that the signals would only serve to let their families know where their boat had gone down.

Both men gripped the rails along the boat's side. A small lifeboat sat onboard, but it would be of little use. Even though they had oars, they would not be strong enough to row against this storm. Charlie looked at the lifeboat bitterly. The shore was not that far away, and under any other circumstances, the lifeboat would save them. But not today.

Suddenly, the sky seemed to grow black. Charlie and Arthur looked up just in time to see a monster wave curl over the top of them. There was a loud *boom*, and then everything was watery and silent for nearly a minute as both men were pounded by the wave and pushed underwater. Gasping and struggling, the men managed to find the rail of the ship again. But it wasn't where it should be. To their horror, Charlie and Arthur realized that their boat had been turned on its side.

"What now, Arthur?" Charlie yelled, his eyes full of terror.

Arthur just shook his head. There was nothing left to do but go down with the ship. They might try to swim to shore, but the currents and waves would surely be too strong.

"I don't know, Charlie. I guess . . . I guess this is it," Arthur said as he gripped the rail desperately.

High on a hill, not far from the shore, a farmer named Bert was watching the storm. He had seen worse storms, but this one had come up more quickly than anything he'd seen before. He peered through a small telescope out to the waves. As he scanned the waves, he was shocked to suddenly see the overturned tugboat. Straining his eyes, Bert could barely make out two figures holding on. Waves were breaking over them as they bounced around in the storm.

What can I do? Bert thought desperately as he paced back and forth on the hill. Each time he looked through his telescope, the little tugboat had sunk further into the sea. In an hour or less, it would sink to the bottom of the ocean. Though the storm was weakening, the seas were still much too rough for the men to swim to safety. *If I could only get to them . . .* Bert thought.

Then a strange idea came to Bert.

In seconds, Bert had dashed to his stables and jumped on the back of his big horse, Shotgun. Slapping the reins against Shotgun's neck, Bert rode his horse down the steep sandy road to the beach.

"Easy, boy. Easy." Bert spoke softly to Shotgun. Though the horse did not balk as he approached the stormy beach, Bert knew he was confused. Still, Shotgun obeyed without hesitation when Bert leaned forward and said "go" into Shotgun's ear. The big horse walked quickly into the ocean. The foamy waves splashed against the horse and his rider, and wind whistled in their ears.

Bert knew his horse could swim because he'd seen him do it several times in the past. But would the horse be brave and strong enough to swim out to the tugboat and carry three men back to shore? There was only one way to find out. Deeper and deeper, Shotgun walked quickly into the ocean until he could walk no longer and began churning his strong legs. Keeping his head above water, the horse seemed to know exactly what his task was. Without a word of direction from his master, Shotgun headed directly toward the sinking boat.

For fifteen minutes, the horse swam against currents, waves, and wind. Bert held on tightly and prayed that Shotgun would not give up.

Finally, Charlie spotted the strange sight of a man riding on the back of a swimming horse. At first, he thought he was seeing things, but then he heard Bert yell up to him.

"There's no time to waste! Untie the lifeboat and drop it in the water. Then the two of you get inside it—Shotgun here will pull you to shore."

The lifeboat was already half under water, but the two men managed to wrestle it out. They set it on the stormy sea, and tossed a rope to Bert who tied it around Shotgun's saddle horn. Thunder crashed, drowning out their words to one another, but within minutes, all three men were being carried toward the shore—Bert on his horse's back, and Charlie and Arthur in the lifeboat. They heard a loud *crack* and *whoosh* and looked back to see the tugboat disappear underwater. Charlie and Arthur had escaped death by only a matter of seconds.

The big horse strained and foamed at the mouth, but he did not give up. The loud wind and crashing waves were terrifying, but Shotgun did not panic or bolt. The shoreline became more and more visible. Closer and closer, until . . . finally! Shotgun's hooves touched sand. He was able to stop swimming and start walking instead.

But the danger wasn't over. Just as it looked as though everyone would make it to shore safely, Shotgun stepped into a deep hole and was swept into a whirlpool. The big horse was literally pulled under water and spun in circles. Bert was thrown from his horse and dragged back out to sea by the strong currents. And Charlie and Arthur held on to the lifeboat as it twisted back and forth, still tied to Shotgun.

But Shotgun fought hard. Kicking and snorting, he finally broke free from the whirlpool and quickly pulled the lifeboat and its two passengers to shore and safety. But where was Bert? Shotgun pawed the beach and stared back out at the stormy sea. His ears twisted back and forth. Then, for just a second, he froze, staring hard at something in the water.

Suddenly, Shotgun bolted back into the ocean, still dragging the empty lifeboat behind him. Swimming with every bit of strength he had left, Shotgun made it to his master's side just in time. Bert fell across his horse's back, gasping for air and holding on to Shotgun's mane. Then, once again, Shotgun swam back to shore. But this time he avoided holes and whirlpools as he found the sand and then galloped ashore.

And just as quickly as the storm had blown in, it disappeared. The three men sat dazed and exhausted on the shore as the sun peeked around the clouds. Shotgun trotted over to Bert and stood beside him, nudging Bert with his nose now and then. The men were silent for a long time.

"That's some miracle horse," Arthur finally said. "I've never seen anything like him."

The two other men just stared at Shotgun and nodded. "A miracle horse"—What more was there to say?

●　●　●

Who can help but snicker at a Chihuahua? They're only about eight inches tall and weigh only six pounds, but Chihuahuas often have the attitude of a trained attack dog. Clearly, they don't think of themselves as tiny—and sometimes that's a good thing.

Lisa Harry owned a little Chihuahua with a big attitude. "Haven" would yap his head off when strangers came to the door, often lunging at ankles and growling threateningly.

"Don't worry. The biggest danger is getting a little dog-slobber on your socks," Lisa would tell visitors who found themselves the focus of Haven's fury. "Haven's all bark and no bite. He thinks he's a big hero, but he's about as dangerous as a gerbil."

But Haven was bound and determined to prove his owner wrong. And one afternoon, he got his chance.

Lisa's two-year-old son, Sean, was out in the backyard toddling around and playing with the pecan nuts that had fallen from a tree. Every so often, Sean would throw one (as well as a two-year-old can) across the yard and laugh hysterically when Haven would chase after it on his stumpy little legs. Lisa kept an eye on both Sean and Haven from the kitchen window as she worked on dinner.

But suddenly, Lisa heard Sean make a noise that was definitely not laughter.

"It was an unbelievable scream," she later told her mother. "It was a sound I'd never heard him make before."

Lisa looked out the window. What she saw froze her blood. In the corner of the yard by an old pile of hay, Sean was being shaken back and forth by a four-foot-long water moccasin—a deadly poisonous snake. Sean had apparently startled the big snake while playing in the hay, and now the snake was attacking.

"I couldn't move," Lisa recalls. "I felt like I was in one of those nightmares where your feet are glued to the ground. I was that scared."

But little Haven was not scared. Immediately, the Chihuahua raced across the yard to Sean. Without hesitating for even a moment, Haven jumped up and braced himself against Sean's leg while pulling at the snake with his teeth. But the snake continued shaking the little boy. In response, Haven clamped his teeth harder around the snake and started shaking back.

After a few seconds of fierce shaking, Haven managed to pull the snake off of Sean. As Lisa ran out to Sean, Haven continued shaking the snake as hard as he could, sprinting around the backyard with the four-foot water moccasin hanging from his little mouth.

Luckily, Sean had not been bitten. The snake had grabbed onto Sean's pants, not his skin. But Lisa rushed him to the hospital just to be sure.

"He's fine," the doctor said after an examination. "But it's a good thing your dog got a hold of that snake when he did. What kind of dog did you say it was—a German shepherd?"

Lisa smiled and kind of rolled her eyes. "Well, not exactly," she said.

Later that evening when Sean and his mother got home, they looked through the window out to the backyard. Lisa feared the worst. She couldn't imagine how Haven could have escaped without getting bitten. And a water moccasin bite on a six-pound dog would definitely be deadly.

But there was Haven in his favorite spot on top of the picnic table, surveying the backyard like the king of the world. Lisa called him inside, and he came prancing in with his head held high. He seemed to know that he had done something remarkable and brave. But in the midst of his gloating, he took a moment to trot over to Sean, check him out, and give him a quick lick. Then he returned to his proud prancing. Lisa watched him, grinning.

"Okay. Come here," she said squatting down to the floor to pet Haven.

"What a *big*, *tough* dog," Lisa said sincerely. "What a hero."

DOCTOR FONZIE

Preview

Four-year-old Joe no longer seems to care about living. When he stops eating and speaking, his parents become increasingly alarmed. Frantic to save their son, Joe's parents take him to meet with a rather unusual "doctor"—a dolphin named Fonzie.

DOCTOR FONZIE

"I'm sorry," the doctor said to Deena and Peter Hoagland. "I'm simply being honest when I say that your son will probably never lead a normal life. He's just suffered too much illness."

"But how do you know that for sure?" Deena asked desperately. "Isn't there anything we can do to try and help him?"

The doctor sighed. Deena and Peter's four-year-old son, Joe, had been born with serious heart problems. These problems required

numerous operations. During the third operation, Joe had had a stroke—a sort of "lightning
storm" in his brain. The stroke had left Joe
unable to move much of the left side of his
body. It had also made it hard for him to speak
or use his hands properly.

"Well, of course, there are many therapies," the doctor suggested, without much
encouragement in his voice. "You might try to
find a speech therapist and a physical therapist.
Joe should be able to regain some movement
if he really tries."

As Deena and Peter wheeled their son
out of the hospital, they were silent. Neither
wanted to voice their anger and frustration in
front of their son. *He may be only four*, Peter
thought to himself, *but I know he can understand what's going on.* He looked down and
smiled at Joe instead. Joe glanced up at his
father, but he did not smile. His eyes were
emotionless and tired.

Over the next few months, the Hoaglands
tried all sorts of traditional therapies to help
Joe move and speak again. But nothing seemed
to work. And to make matters worse, Peter
had been right—Joe did seem to understand
what was going on, and it was making him
very sad. As Deena pushed him around in
his stroller, she could see Joe watching other
young children at play. His eyes would follow them chasing balls and scrambling around

playgrounds. Sometimes she would see Joe look at his own helpless hands after he had watched two children playing catch.

Before long, Joe became withdrawn and depressed. Deena and Peter tried to cheer him up with toys and extra attention, but Joe was slowly giving up. Day by day, he became less interested in life, and he made no attempts to move his withering arms and legs. Then one day, he no longer wanted to eat. He sat very still, staring straight ahead. He barely responded to questions or even affection.

"What are we going to do, Peter?" Deena sat with her husband at the kitchen table one night.

"I don't know," Peter answered honestly as he wiped away a tear. The two of them sat holding hands and talking until very late.

"You know," Deena said at one point, "I remember how thrilled Joe was when the nurse brought in a puppy for him to play with one time after an operation. I think it was the only time I've ever seen him smile in the hospital."

Peter nodded, but he wasn't sure what Deena meant. "So you think we should bring home a dog . . . ?"

"Not really," Deena said with a funny expression on her face. "I was actually thinking of something I had read in the paper the other day. Now wait until I'm finished before calling me crazy."

Deena went on to describe a research center in Florida where dolphins were used to help kids with physical, emotional, and mental problems. No one could really explain why, but for some reason when children swam and played with the dolphins, the children got better. And the dolphins were not "trained" to pay attention to sick children—it came naturally to the intelligent ocean animals. They seemed to understand that something was wrong. They gently and playfully nudged their young patients out of depression, out of silence, and back into the world.

Peter stared at Deena. "Crazy?" he finally said. "That's about the most sane thing I've heard in a while. Let's go to Florida."

Sitting on the dock at "Dolphins Plus" in Key Largo, Florida, Joe still looked sad and bored. His mother held him so that he could sit up and dangle his feet in the water. Suddenly, there was a little ripple in the water, then a fin cutting through, and then a big grinning dolphin popped his head above water and chattered at Joe. It was "Fonzie," a 650-pound dolphin who had been helping children for years.

At first, Joe was frightened. He'd never been so close to such a large animal. But Fonzie was gentle. He pushed his nose against Joe's feet and then swam away. When he was about twenty yards out, Fonzie rose out of the water again and chattered at Joe, nodding his head and splashing. Joe stared, open-mouthed and curious. What *was* that? And why was it laughing so loudly? When Fonzie came back and nudged Joe's feet again, Joe no longer seemed afraid. In fact, Joe looked up at his mother and did something she hadn't seen him do in months—he giggled.

From that day on, Fonzie would rush over to the dock as soon as Joe and his parents arrived. Fonzie seemed to have a special connection with Joe, and he was even seen pushing other dolphins out of the way so that he could become Joe's favorite. And Joe soon came to love letting Fonzie blow water on him and feeling Fonzie bump his feet. A couple of times, Joe even leaned forward to pat Fonzie on his long, smooth bottle-shaped snout.

One afternoon, a marine scientist who worked at Dolphins Plus came over to Joe with a bucket of fish.

"Want to try and give your friend a snack?" she asked, kneeling down next to Joe. She grabbed a few small fish out of the bucket and tossed them out to Fonzie, who leaped high into the air to catch them. Joe giggled and tried to reach toward the bucket for the fish. But he was unable to control his movements. Doctors had told Joe's parents again and again that Joe *could* learn to use his hands and arms again if he'd only try. But Joe had been too depressed to try—until now. Joe awkwardly plunged his hands into the fish bucket. Over and over, he attempted to grasp a fish, but his hands weren't ready yet.

"Remember—open your fingers and then close your fingers," the scientist said, taking Joe's hand and showing him. "We'll try again tomorrow."

That night, Deena and Peter heard some strange sounds coming from Joe's room. It sounded like a child's voice, but Joe had barely spoken in months. They tiptoed to Joe's door and listened carefully.

"Open fingers. Close fingers . . ." Joe's small voice repeated the words for nearly an hour.

Once Joe mastered grabbing fish and throwing them to Fonzie, he was suddenly eager to try playing all sorts of games with his dolphin friend. Within only a few months, Joe went from being a sad, withdrawn child who was unwilling to even try moving his arms and legs, to an excited and increasingly active little boy. He was able to lift a ball above his head and toss it to Fonzie. He was able to shoot a water gun, shrieking with laughter every time Fonzie flew out of the water and became a "target." And he chattered and talked to Fonzie nearly as much as Fonzie chattered to him.

Finally, the day came when Joe would get a chance to enter Fonzie's world.

"Okay. Now don't be afraid; you know that Fonzie's your pal. He would never hurt you," one of the workers at Dolphins Plus said as he tightened the lifejacket around Joe's waist. Joe looked down at the water doubtfully. It had been fun playing from the dock, but what would being in the water be like?

"Ready?" the worker asked as he lifted Joe up to lower him into the water.

"Ready," Joe whispered.

Joe bobbed in the warm saltwater for only a few seconds before Fonzie approached him slowly. Fonzie lifted his head out of the water to greet his friend face to face. He gently moved forward to touch his nose to Joe's. Joe grinned and Fonzie chattered. Then Fonzie turned around so that Joe could grab his fin—and the two of them took off for a ride around the bay. Joe had never moved so quickly. Suddenly, all the discomfort and awkwardness in his arms and legs seemed to disappear. He laughed out loud and hugged Fonzie. As the two zoomed by the dock, Joe waved to his parents. Peter shook his head and smiled. "After all those doctors and therapies, who would have guessed it? A dolphin has saved our son."

Fifteen years later, Deena and Peter Hoagland stood on the edge of a dock.

Speaking quietly, they reassured a young, emotionally disturbed girl that the dolphin swimming up to her would not hurt her. Not long after their experience with Fonzie and Joe, Deena and Peter had sold their home, loaded up the moving van, and relocated to Key West, Florida. They started their own "dolphin therapy" center and worked with dozens of children every year.

As Deena and Peter spoke gently to the girl, a tall young man came strolling out to the dock. He was carrying a few textbooks and eating a slice of pizza. It was Joe Hoagland, coming home after his first day of classes at the local community college.

"So how'd it go?" his father asked him.

"Pretty good," Joe said as he ate half the slice of pizza in one bite. "I really like my biology class. But history's gonna be a pain. So much homework . . . It doesn't seem fair. When am I gonna have time for basketball?"

Out in the water, a familiar head popped up and chattered loudly at Joe.

"Quit laughing, Fonz! It's not funny!" Joe shouted out to his friend.

Peter Hoagland looked at his son and smiled. *Never lead a normal life?* he thought. *It doesn't get much more normal than this.*

AFTER HURRICANE KATRINA

Preview

After Hurricane Katrina, 50,000 pets became strays. News stories showed panicked dogs and lost cats on rooftops. But some animals beat the odds. Here are two stories that prove that when an animal's will to survive meets human kindness, great things happen.

AFTER HURRICANE KATRINA

—1—

Terri woke up suddenly in the backseat of an old car. Five months pregnant, she had felt her baby kick right in the middle of a dream. In her dream, Terri was in a nice house, resting in a soft bed. But as her eyes adjusted to the early morning darkness, Terri remembered; she remembered the hurricane that had blown out all the windows in her apartment. She remembered the eerie night when the water began rushing into New Orleans and she had to escape to the rooftop. She remembered the strangers who came by in a boat and rowed her to safety.

But at the shelter, they had told her she could not bring in her dog, Tasha.

"But . . . but I can't leave her," Terri had said. She looked at the little black and white terrier. Tasha was wagging her tail and holding up one paw—something she always did when she was unsure of what was happening.

"Oh, she'll be fine," the woman at the shelter assured Terri. "We have volunteers who will take care of her."

"So," Terri said slowly, "You mean that after I leave the shelter, I can pick her up?"

The woman looked away and then back at Terri. "Well, no. What I meant is that they will try to find a home for her."

"But that's not what I want to do . . ." Terri began.

"Look," the woman said, sounding tired and a little irritated. "There are 50,000 lost, stray, and injured animals in New Orleans right now. There are thousands more that cannot live in the shelters with their owners. We're doing the best we can do."

Terri was silent for a moment. Her eyes filled with tears at the thought of handing

Tasha off to a stranger and just hoping for the best.

"But someone will find her a good home, right?" Terri asked, wiping away a tear.

The woman sighed. "I'm sorry—I really am," she said a little more kindly. "But you should know the truth. Very, very few people in New Orleans are looking to adopt pets right now. Most people are just like you; they're simply trying to find a way to survive and a place to land."

Terri didn't ask any more questions. She knew what the woman was really saying— Tasha would be kept in a hot and uncomfortable kennel for a week and then she would be put to sleep. Terri bent over and picked up her little dog.

"Thanks, anyway," Terri said quietly as she turned to leave. The woman came up behind Terri and placed her hand on her shoulder.

"Remember, we're here, and we want to help you," the woman said. Terri stopped and turned around. The woman looked down at Terri's stomach. "And also remember—your unborn child's life is more important than your dog's."

It was these words that Terri kept hearing repeated in her head as she waited for the sun to come up that morning. Like so many people after the hurricane, Terri was broke and had no place to go. She had lived for three weeks now in the backseat of an old abandoned Ford Taurus. She went to the shelter every day for food, and they had given her some medicine and blankets, too. But she had not been willing to give up her best friend, Tasha. Still, she knew that there was something more important in her life now.

Terri had found Tasha eight and a half months earlier. On a dreary December afternoon, Terri had watched as a car full of teenagers had slowed down and tossed a small dog out onto the city sidewalk. Then the car sped away, laughter and music spilling out of the windows. Terri rushed over and picked up the shivering terrier.

"You poor thing," Terri said, looking at the hungry and filthy dog. Even in its frightened state, the little dog reached out a paw and gently tapped Terri on the nose twice.

"Okay," Terri said with a smile. "Since you've asked, I'll take care of you."

Over the months, the two became inseparable. Terri nursed the dog she named Tasha back to perfect health. And Tasha comforted Terri when Terri's boyfriend immediately disappeared when he found out she was pregnant with their baby.

"Looks like we both know somethin' about being abandoned," Terri had said to Tasha. Tasha had just wagged her tail in agreement.

But that had been five months ago. Since then, Terri's world had been turned inside out following Katrina. She had lost her job at a restaurant that had been destroyed, her apartment was no longer standing, and her bank account was empty. But all of this paled in comparison to the fact that Terri was only four months away from giving birth. She knew in her heart that she could not continue to live in an old car.

Like every morning, Tasha awoke, stretched, yawned loudly a few times, and then settled on top of Terri's growing belly. But unlike most mornings, Terri did not play with the dog and say silly things to her. Instead, Terri sadly stroked Tasha's head a couple of times and whispered, "I'm sorry."

Later that morning, Terri packed up her few belongings and headed slowly over to the shelter, Tasha happily following behind her. Wisely, Terri had decided that she must move to the shelter during these last months of her pregnancy in order to receive proper care and be in a safe environment. Still, it hurt her all the way through to have to give up the dog she loved so much. She couldn't bear to think about what was probably going to be Tasha's fate.

"I know it sounds stupid, but this is the hardest choice I've ever had to make," Terri said through tears to a volunteer. The volunteer was a young woman named Susan who was about the same age as Terri.

"It doesn't sound stupid at all," Susan said, shaking her head. "I know exactly how you feel."

"Please, then," Terri said. "*Please* find Tasha a home."

The volunteer saw a look in Terri's eyes that she would never forget—a mix of desperation, love, and selfless sacrifice.

"I promise you that I'll try my hardest," Susan said.

And Susan kept her promise. Although she was swamped with work at the shelter, she made phone calls, sent emails, and generally asked around. Didn't anyone want an adorable, well-behaved little terrier? But again and again, the answer would be the same— "We'd love to take her, but we just can't." Susan felt the clock ticking. If she couldn't find Tasha a new home in a week, she would have to have Tasha put to sleep.

Finally, Susan got an encouraging phone call. The grandson of an elderly woman who lived about twenty-five miles outside of New Orleans had seen an email posting about the terrier.

"My Grandma Mae lost a dog a while back. It was some sort of little black and white dog, too," the grandson explained. "So, maybe having a new dog that kinda looks the same would cheer her up."

That afternoon, Susan made the twenty-five mile drive to a small town set back in the bayou. When she pulled down the long dirt drive, she could see Mae sitting on the wooden porch. Mae waved and got to her feet slowly. Susan glanced over at Tasha, who had ridden the whole way quietly curled up on an old blanket. Tasha had been one sad dog since she had been separated from Terri. Susan had only seen her feebly wag her tail a couple of times, and Tasha was barely eating anything.

"Maybe you'll have someone to love you here," Susan said to Tasha with a little pat. "But you might want to perk up a little bit."

Susan parked her car and picked up Tasha to carry her over to Mae. But then, the most amazing thing happened. Susan had barely stepped out of her car when Tasha suddenly sprang from her arms like a crazed dog and went scampering as fast as she could up to Mae. Tasha then leaped into Mae's arms as Mae gave a whoop of surprise.

"I am absolutely not believing this!" Mae was saying over and over again as Susan ran over to the porch.

"Oh, I am so sorry. She's usually not so . . ." Susan began.

"Sorry?" Mae asked with a laugh. "This is a real miracle. I never thought I'd see my little Elly again!"

Susan stood there stunned as the story unfolded. About nine months earlier, Mae had driven into New Orleans to do some Christmas shopping. As always, Elly came along and "guarded" the car. But this time when Mae returned to her car, Elly had disappeared without a trace. Mae had been heartbroken, wondering what on earth had happened to her companion.

Somehow, against all imaginable odds, "Elly" had been rescued by Terri a couple of weeks later, after a group of high school kids had grown tired of the little dog. And in a strange twist of fortune brought on by a hurricane, the same dog would be rescued again by its original owner. As Elly ran in circles barking happily and wagging her tail, Susan could only shake her head and smile.

That evening, Susan sat down with Terri and told her the amazing story. Terri could only laugh and cry and keep repeating "What a miracle!"

"And Mae says you're welcome to come out and visit whenever you want," Susan said.

Terri thought about that for a while and then said, "You know, I may do that at some point. But right now," and here she rubbed her stomach and smiled, "I have some more important things to take care of."

—2—

Like thousands of other families in New Orleans, the Petersons were told that they must leave their home. The floodwaters were rising higher and higher, and if they stayed in their house, they might all drown. But also like thousands of other families, the Petersons did not want to leave their family pet behind.

"This is a mandatory evacuation!" the man in the uniform shouted through the megaphone. "You must leave your residence. There are no exceptions."

"Can't we please bring our cat?" Jeff Peterson shouted from the porch where water was already seeping through the doorway.

"No!" the man bellowed. "Pets must remain behind. That's the law. You have fifteen minutes. Remember—this evacuation is *mandatory*. You are required by law to leave your homes in fifteen minutes."

Jeff and Hannah Peterson looked at their daughter, who was already panicking.

"But Daddy," seven-year-old Sara cried, tugging at her father's hand, "we can't leave Smokey behind. She's gonna have her babies! Can't we hide her in a suitcase?"

Jeff leaned over and picked up his daughter. "Don't you worry. Smokey will be all right. We'll fix her a nice box with blankets way up on the second floor. We'll put out lots of food and water for her—and we'll be back in just a few days. Everything's going to be fine."

Sara considered this for a moment, but then her face grew dark again.

"But what if the water goes higher than the second floor?"

Jeff looked helplessly at his wife. Outside, the man with the megaphone was shouting "Ten minutes!"

Hannah Peterson took her daughter from her husband. "Come on. Let's get Smokey's nest ready while Daddy gets some other things together." Hannah and Sara prepared a large box with an old pillow and a blanket stuffed in it. Then they poured three bowls of cat food and an entire bucket of water. All of this was carried up to the bedroom on the second floor before they looked for Smokey.

Smokey, as usual, was sleeping on the sofa near the front door. Megaphones, floods, and a crying child didn't seem to rattle her at all. Tremendously pregnant, she was laying on her back with all four white-tipped paws in the air. When Hannah reached down to pick her up, Smokey immediately began a rumbling purr.

"Will she have her kittens while we're gone?" Sara asked as they carried Smokey upstairs.

"She might, sweetie."

"But how will she know what to do

without us?" Sara's face was full of worry.

"Oh, she'll know," Hannah said with a smile. "Mother cats always do what's best for their kittens. Everything will be fine."

But Hannah wasn't so sure. No one knew how high the water would rise. With the levees broken, the Gulf of Mexico could fill the streets of New Orleans. The water, in fact, could rise up to or even above the second floor. So when her daughter wasn't looking, Hannah opened a closet door and piled a few boxes up to the shelves. *Just in case*, Hannah thought. *She can escape to the top shelf if she needs to.*

Two days later and 60 miles away in a prison for women, Sunny Miller was watching the news with a couple of other inmates. An overhead view of New Orleans was showing thousands of homes nearly covered in water—only the rooftops peeked through.

"Wish there was something we could do," Sunny said to no one in particular.

"Yeah, right. Like there's anything we can do here behind bars. Like anyone would want our help," a much younger woman replied with a laugh. "Ain't our problem anyways."

Sunny didn't say anything. Years ago, she had felt the same way as that young woman. She hadn't cared about anyone or anything but herself. It was that attitude that had allowed her to sell drugs to kids, to lose her temper easily, and, one night fifteen years ago, to shoot a stranger for fifty dollars.

Sunny continued to watch the coverage. Film of one rooftop showed a wet, terrified dog running back and forth and yelping. The camera zoomed in, and suddenly two puppies appeared alongside the frantic dog. Tears sprang to Sunny's eyes as she watched the helpless animals.

"Three more victims of this tragedy," the reporter's voice was saying sadly. "New Orleans is simply overwhelmed by the thousands of pets that owners were forced, sometimes at gunpoint, to leave behind. Nearly all these animals will be abandoned since most of the owners will not be allowed to return to their homes for weeks. And many owners will simply never return at all. The local animal shelters are rescuing hundreds of animals, but the shelters only have so much room—and that room is running out."

Suddenly, Sunny's expression changed. A strange smile crept across her face.

"What are you smiling at?" the younger woman asked.

"Got an idea. And I think it's a good one," Sunny replied.

Hannah Peterson had been right about two things: the floodwater had indeed reached into the second floor, and Smokey did do what was best for her kittens. Smokey had given birth to four grey kittens with white paws the very afternoon that the Petersons had left. She had cleaned them carefully and curled up with them in the box that Hannah and her daughter had prepared.

But several hours later, Smokey sat up, her nose sniffing and her green eyes darting around the room. The sharp smell of dirty saltwater was in the air. And underneath the doors came hissing streams of black water. Immediately, Smokey began searching for higher ground. Within minutes, she discovered the piled boxes that led to the closet shelves. And one by one, Smokey dragged her kittens by the neck to the top shelf. There, she rested with her kittens, but she would not close her eyes. Below her, the water continued to rise, gurgling and hissing and smelling dangerous. Smokey began pacing the top shelf, crying softly.

When the water reached within a few feet of the top shelf, Smokey began clawing and biting at a loose vent cover near the top of the closet. The water crept closer. Just as the water began wetting her paws, Smokey knocked the vent cover off. In a flash, she began hauling her kittens through the vent that led to a crawlspace that eventually opened into the attic. One, two, three kittens were safe in the dry attic. But when Smokey returned for the fourth, she was too late. The water had swept the tiny kitten away without a trace.

"Yes, I think it's a great idea." The assistant prison warden was nodding as she spoke with Sunny. "I'll give a call to the New Orleans Humane Society and see what they think."

Sunny just smiled.

"Now, you know that this will be a lot of work, right?" the warden asked.

"I'd be glad to do it," Sunny answered.

"And you can't get too attached," the warden also warned.

"I'll try not to," Sunny said. But she wondered if that would be harder than the work itself.

Jeff Peterson had been wrong about two things. The Petersons did not return to their home after a few days. In fact, they were not allowed to return for weeks. Their entire neighborhood had been destroyed, and the poisonous mold and mud that covered the homes forced residents to stay away much longer than they had expected.

Jeff had seen pictures of their neighborhood—the water had risen nearly to the roofs of all the houses. He hugged his young daughter as she cried and explained that cats go to heaven, too. Because, after all, there was no way Smokey could have survived.

But this was where Jeff was wrong, too. Several days after the flood, searcher-rescuers entered the Peterson's home looking for trapped people or animals. They were nearly finished with their search when one rescuer heard a high-pitched sound above his head.

"Where's it coming from?" he asked, looking around. "I could swear it sounds like a cat, but I can't figure out where it would be."

But soon enough, the rescuers found their way into the attic and followed the meows. Finally they found Smokey and her three kittens huddled in a corner—alive, but just barely.

"Okay, let's get them over to the shelter at the Humane Society," the rescuer said, knowing it would be impossible to track down the family. Then he sighed and shook his head—"I just hope they have room."

Sunny Miller sat on the floor of an old prison storage building that hadn't been used in years. She was staring at the first residents of the prison's temporary "overflow emergency pet shelter": three impossibly small gray kittens with white paws and their purring mother. Just that morning, the New Orleans Humane Society had called the assistant warden to tell her that a family of cats had been rescued from an attic.

Sunny had immediately gone to work putting together bedding, food, and litter boxes. She cleaned out the storage building and scrubbed the windows so that the kittens would have sunlight to play in. She even made some toys out of aluminum foil for the kittens to bat around once they got older. Now she was just sitting quietly and marveling at how the mother and her kittens had survived. Across from Sunny sat the young inmate who had originally laughed at the idea of helping. She had a funny look on her face, almost tender, as she stared at the kittens.

"They've sure been through a lot and yet . . . yet . . ." The young woman seemed to be searching for the right words, looking a bit embarrassed about being emotional. "Well, they don't give up very easily, that's for sure."

"They've had a rough journey," Sunny agreed.

"But now they're here, so we get a chance to make things okay for them until they're adopted, right?" the young woman asked as she barely touched one of the kitten's tiny paws.

"Yes," Sunny said, "But only until then. So don't get too close to them."

"That's okay. It's nice to be needed for a little while, I guess."

"It certainly is," Sunny said with a smile.

THE LAST HUNT

Preview

A boy becomes lost in a rugged wilderness during a hunting trip. As the sun disappears, he hears a large animal in the dark getting closer and closer. What suddenly emerges from the woods surprises the boy. And what happens later that night amazes him.

THE LAST HUNT

I know these mountains like the back of my hand. I'm fifteen now, and I've been hunting ducks and geese and deer back in here since I was old enough to aim a shotgun. There's nothing quite like the rush of getting a bird or deer in your sights, quietly steadying your gun, and then squeezing that trigger, praying that it hits the mark. And I'm a pretty good shot. Not too many deer have ever walked away from me once I spot them.

Anyway, as I was saying, I know everything about these mountains and woods for miles and miles. I know the secret paths that lead to the best duck ponds, and I know where the deer go to rest at night so that I can be ready for them in the morning. So that's why I can't figure out what's going on. I left my dad and my uncle on the main trail just an hour ago because I was following some geese. I mean, I leave the main trail all the time. It's no big deal. That's why this is so weird . . . I think I'm lost.

I left some sticks and markers back in a big field to show me the way back to the main trail, but now I can't find them anywhere. In fact, I guess I've wandered so far that the field is nowhere to be found. And you know what's kind of scary? Just now I realized that I have been walking in a circle. I recognize this huge oak tree—it's the same one I passed about forty-five minutes ago.

But I'll be fine. It's still another hour or so until sunset, so I'm sure I'll either find the trail or hear my dad and uncle calling for me. Plus, since I'm in a different part of the woods, I just saw something I hardly ever get to see. Out by a little group of trees were two elk, and one had a huge set of antlers. I raised my gun and got the biggest elk in my sights. I even put my finger on the trigger. Man, I would give any-thing to be able to take that big beast down. What a trophy that would be! But this shotgun isn't big enough. Dad says I can get a rifle next year. Then that elk had better watch out.

Is that thunder? Great. Just what I need. I only wore a thin jacket this morning because it wasn't supposed to rain. As usual, my dad kept nagging me to pack a rain suit, an extra sweater, a hat. You know how parents are—I'd have to haul a whole suitcase along behind me to make him happy. But now I wish I had at least brought a rain jacket. I'm getting soaked to the skin, and it's not getting any warmer now that the sun is beginning to set.

Where *are* they? Why can't I hear my dad and uncle calling for me? The sun is nearly gone now, and there's no way I'll be able to find my way back in the dark. And if I have to spend the whole night out here alone . . . well, I don't even want to think about that. I'll send a few shots up into the air. They'll hear them and know where I am. That always works.

Okay, no one's coming for me. It's been an hour since I fired those shots, and all I've heard is some more distant thunder and some not-so-distant howling. Wolves and coyotes roam these fields at night looking for food, and I doubt they'd turn me down if they found me. Good thing I've got my gun . . . but wait—I only have one shot left! I must have fired off more rounds into the air than I'd thought. One shot left. Well, it had better be a life-or-death situation before I fire that last shot. I think the howling is getting closer.

Now there's ice and snow falling. It's only October, and we don't usually get snow until November, but I guess this is just my lucky night. I'm so cold that I can't stop shaking. My jacket and shirt are still damp from the rainfall. What I need is a fire, but I left all my fire stuff at home, too, because I didn't think I'd need it—just like my rain suit or a sweater. If it keeps snowing, I don't know what will happen. I read about a guy who got lost just last year, not too far from here. He wandered off the trail, and then it began snowing. They found him frozen to death two days later—little icicles on his eyes and his skin all blue. But all I've got to do is stay awake and keep moving. Just stay awake . . .

What was *that*!? Just beyond these trees, something is moving. And whatever it is, it sounds big. Oh no—there's more than one. I can hear them getting closer on either side of me. They're making a loud breathing sound and stomping the ground. I've got my gun lifted, but my fingers are useless. My hands are so cold that I can't wrap my finger around the trigger. Closer . . . closer . . . I can hear them coming straight for me, snarling and panting. I have to shoot, but I can't . . .

You are kidding me. I have to laugh out loud when I finally see the two animals that have been terrorizing me. It's just two big, dumb, harmless elk. Probably the same two I had seen out in the field earlier. They're about as dangerous as ducks and nearly as stupid. That's why elk are great to hunt—they're not smart enough to run away. They'll just stand and stare at you like these two are doing.

But this is kind of weird. These elk don't seem to be afraid of me at all. They walk right up to me and watch me shivering as though they're trying to figure out what I'm doing. The smaller one even touches his long, furry nose to my arm and licks it. *Shoo! Leave!* I suddenly yell. It just gives me the creeps a little to have these two big animals staring at me and checking me out. But they don't budge. I wave my arms in the air and shout the rudest things I can think of at them. Finally, they disappear slowly back into the darkness of the woods, but I can hear them snorting and pawing not too far away.

It must be nearly midnight by now. I know I should keep walking back and forth, but I am so unbelievably tired and hungry. Plus, I think I'd be warmer if I just curled up against this tree so it could block the wind. This is better. I'll just keep moving my arms and legs so that I don't fall asleep. Sleep will mean freezing to

death . . . all alone in the middle of nowhere
. . . wolves creeping slowly toward me . . . ice
sealing my eyes . . . snow gently covering me
up . . . and . . . and . . .

Wake up! I fell asleep! I could die this way.
I have *got* to stay awake until the sunrise. But
hold on a second. I can see the first rays of sunlight way up in the sky. I must have been asleep
for hours. So why am I so warm? Am I already
dead? And I smell something strange—like wet
fur.

Oh, this can't be real. I must be dreaming.
But I'm not. On either side of me, with their
backs pressed against my body, are the two elk.
Their warmth and closeness have kept me from
freezing to death. This is unbelievable. Had
they been in the woods watching me, waiting
for the right time to save me? I reach out to pet
their soft, strong backs. They awaken and raise
their big heads to look at me. The one with the
antlers stares into my eyes for a long moment.
Then both elk slowly get to their feet while
making soft, high-pitched calls to each other.
They stretch and snort, and then they trot off
into the woods, disappearing down a snowy
hillside.

A dog barks. Loud voices are calling my
name, and I recognize the calls of my dad and
uncle.

"Over here!" I yell in their direction. I hear footsteps running toward me.

"You're alive! Thank God." My dad wraps his arms around me and hugs me for a long time. Then he pulls away and looks at me strangely.

"Are you all right?" he asks.

"I—I'm fine," I answer, hardly believing it myself.

"But where did you find shelter?" one of the rescue team workers asks, looking around the snowy woods.

"I didn't really find shelter. It, or they, found me."

Everyone looks at me as if I must be a little wacky from spending a night alone in the freezing woods. I take a deep breath and tell them about the elk. There's a long silence when I finish. Finally, one of the rescue workers clears his throat and speaks.

"Son, I truly don't know how you lived through last night. But you obviously imagined the elk. Exposure to extreme conditions can make you see things. Elk are shy animals—they would never do something like that."

I just shake my head and point back to the area where I had slept. The men walk over and stare at the ground. Surrounding the three depressions on the ground (two elk-sized and one human-sized) are elk hoofprints. The prints lead back down into the woods, just as I had described.

The hike back to town is a quiet one. Everyone is thinking about the elk, I guess. I know I am. About halfway back, we all stop to rest in the warm sun and have something to eat. Before we leave, I set my shotgun in the grass by some boulders.

"Don't forget your gun," my dad says, pointing to the grass.

"Don't want it anymore," I say.

"Well," he says slowly, "I guess after last night's adventure, you're ready for a rifle."

"Don't want a rifle either," I say quickly. My dad gives me a questioning look.

"I won't ever be going hunting again." I start walking and don't look at my dad. He's been hunting all his life. Just like his dad and his granddad.

"Because you got lost?" he asks. "Are you afraid to hunt now just because of that?"

I stop walking and face my father. "I'm not *afraid* of anything," I say. "All I know is that two wild animals saved my life last night. The least I can do is help to save theirs."

My dad and I walk in silence for a long way. I imagine he's disappointed in me. But at one point, I hear him stop for a moment along a little ridge. I look at him and he's grinning.

"What?" I ask.

My dad looks at me for a minute and says,

"I was just about your age when my father gave me a rifle for elk hunting. I always hated shooting them, to tell you the truth. It just felt wrong. But I was worried that my father would think I was afraid if I told him that."

My dad looks out over the valley and shakes his head, smiling. "That's just about right that it takes my *own* son to get me to finally admit that."

"So you're going to stop hunting?" I ask carefully.

At that moment a startled group of geese rises up from the pond below. My father instinctively reaches for his gun and then looks at me. He laughs a short laugh and puts his hand on my shoulder.

"Well, for elk, anyway," he says as we head down the trail for home.

JUNIOR

Preview

When a tornado tears through a neighborhood, a little crow is blown into Jack's kitchen. Jack's first words to the crow are, "I don't even like birds." But the little bird's big personality grows on Jack. This is the story of their friendship.

JUNIOR

"Quick! Get inside NOW!"

Jack yelled across the roar of the wind to his friend, Tom, who was standing in the backyard staring up at the sky and holding a camera. Tom was steadying himself against the wind by leaning against a young oak tree, but he looked as though he might blow away at any moment.

"I've gotta film the tornado!" Tom shouted back to Jack. Tom and Jack had been friends for twenty years, and Jack could not remember a time when Tom had not been a daredevil about weather—he tempted lightning, chased tornadoes, and ran out in hailstorms. Once, he even swam out into the ocean during the eye of a hurricane. Now, taking pictures of storms had become Tom's profession.

"Come on, Tom!" Jack yelled back. "It's too dangerous. It's getting too close!"

Tom just waved at Jack and shook his head. From what seemed like only a few blocks away, Jack could hear crashing, booming, and the popping of electrical transformers. Tornado sirens were shrieking all over the place. Jack called to his friend one more time, and then he dashed inside the house and ran down to the basement. Pulling a heavy pillow over his head, Jack swore and muttered to himself about his friend. *That idiot!* he thought. *This time he's going to get himself killed for sure.*

From the downstairs room, Jack could hear glass shattering somewhere above. The howl of the wind seemed to grow louder for a few minutes. But then, suddenly, the noise ended. Except for the light drumming of rain, there was no sound of the terrible storm that Jack was certain had destroyed his house and killed his friend. Jack sat and listened nervously for nearly twenty minutes. Finally, with a heavy sigh and shaking hands, Jack slowly climbed up the stairs. But when he opened the door and peeked out, an unexpected sight met his eyes.

Sitting at the kitchen table, amid some broken glass, was Tom. He was calmly drinking a Coke and staring into a cardboard box with a funny expression on his face. When Tom heard the basement door open, he glanced over at Jack as though nothing unusual had just taken place. Then he motioned for him to come over.

"Look at this," Tom said, pointing into the box. "What is it?"

Jack looked around the room in a daze. Actually, there was not much damage—just a broken window in the kitchen. The tornado must have missed his house.

Jack looked back over at Tom. "Huh? What are you talking about? I can't believe you're still alive . . . didn't you even get a scratch?"

Without looking away from the box, Tom stuck his elbow up in the air to show two band-aids. Then he motioned again for Jack to come and look inside the box. Shaking his head, Jack wandered over and peered in. Sitting in the bottom of the box was a very wet and bedraggled baby bird. Its eyes were closed and it was shaking very hard.

"What is it?" Tom asked again.

"Well, it pretty much looks like a bird," Jack said matter-of-factly.

"I know *that*," Tom said, glaring briefly at

his friend. "I mean, what kind of bird?"

"Hmmm . . . probably a crow. It's all black, and it has a huge beak," Jack replied. "Where did you find it?"

"Right here in your kitchen," Tom answered, standing up and picking up his camera. "It must have blown out of a nest and right through that broken window."

"Where do you think you're going?" Jack asked as Tom headed quickly toward the back door.

"Sorry man, but I have to follow that storm. It totally missed us here, so I'm headed in its direction to see if I can get some pictures."

"But what about this . . . this . . . baby crow?" Jack shouted after his friend, who was already getting in his car.

Tom paused and looked back at Jack for a moment.

"Yeah. Well, good luck with all that," Tom yelled back with a friendly wave as he pulled out of the driveway.

Jack stood in his back yard staring up at the trees in search of a crow's nest. Since it was still early spring, most of the trees were still half bare, so it would be easy to spot something as monstrous as a crow's nest.

"Not even a freaking sparrow's nest," Jack muttered to himself as he inspected the last tree. Jack knew that if he returned the bird to its nest, the parents would continue to care for it, but he would have to find the nest first. Sheepishly, Jack began wandering through several neighbors' yards, trying to look casual as he stared up at the trees. Finally, after about an hour of searching, Jack grudgingly accepted the fact that every nest in the entire neighborhood had probably been blown right out of its tree. Jack was the reluctant owner of a scared baby crow.

Returning home, Jack sat and stared at the little bird for a long time. It wasn't a newborn, but it wasn't quite big enough to fly yet. Its head was still fuzzy, and its beak still looked laughably large for its face.

"I don't even like birds," Jack said wearily to the crow. The crow opened one eyeball and blinked at Jack.

"And even people who like birds don't like crows," Jack continued, looking into the crow's one opened eye. The crow let out a pathetic little croak. In spite of himself, Jack had to smile.

"Crows are loud, rude, and dirty—the sworn enemies of farmers worldwide," Jack concluded more gently now. The baby crow had opened both eyes and was looking right at Jack. Slowly, Jack reached into the box and stretched out a finger toward the bird. Immediately, the little crow opened its mouth wide and started squawking.

"Whoa!" Jack said, pulling his hand back quickly. "Either you're mad at me for those insults, or you're hungry. I'm guessing you're hungry, so . . ."

Jack poked around his kitchen, trying to imagine what a scared, abandoned crow might like. He gathered a slice of pizza, a chicken wing, lettuce, chocolate pudding, and two very old strawberries. All of these he chopped into little pieces (except the pudding, of course) and began dangling them in front of the crow. Within thirty seconds, Jack discovered that a baby crow, like a baby human, will simply spit out anything it doesn't like. Soon, the cardboard box was covered with rejected pizza, lettuce, and pudding. The crow shook its head, ruffled its feathers, and stared at Jack as though he were an idiot. The strawberries were met with only vague interest.

But then, the chicken was introduced. Instantly, the crow gobbled the little piece down and then burst forth with a series of deafening squawks and wing flappings.

"All right, all right! Calm down!" Jack mumbled as he rushed back to the refrigerator to retrieve more chicken. "Geez. What kind of bird prefers to dine on other birds, anyway?"

After eating what seemed like an immense pile of chopped-up chicken, the little crow clamped his big beak shut and stared with glazed eyes at Jack. Within minutes, it tucked its fuzzy head under a wing and nodded off. Jack plopped down in a chair, exhausted. It had been quite an afternoon. He fired up his laptop in order to do a little reading about what in the world to do with a baby crow. On a site for abandoned and lost animals, he read, "Baby crows, depending on their age, need to be fed every thirty minutes to every few hours. The younger the crow, the more often it will need food."

There is NO way I am going to feed this crow every couple of hours, Jack thought as he glared at his computer and continued reading: "Favorite foods of young crows include raw peas and steamed green beans, peanut butter mixed with mashed potatoes, softly scrambled eggs, soft fruits, and chicken. Chicken should be raw or very lightly roasted with sesame seeds."

"That does it!" Jack said out loud as he snapped his computer shut. "I am absolutely *not* going to prepare steamed beans and sesame chicken for a crow who barged into my kitchen uninvited." He stomped over to the box and looked into it with a scowl. The little crow was sleeping soundly, and the slightest bit of a snore rumbled from under its wing. Jack sighed.

A week later, Jack was standing at his stove

at 4:00 a.m. stirring a pan of softly-scrambled eggs. The crow, who Jack had simply named "Junior," was perched on the side of its box, belting out a rapid-fire collection of "caw" sounds. Junior's "caw" was not quite perfect, but it was loud.

"You need to grow some wings and fly away!" Jack yelled, shaking a spoon at Junior. Junior cawed back, and Jack flicked an egg-shell across the room at him. But the truth was, Jack had quickly grown very fond of the little crow. He had never had a pet before, and he was touched by how much the helpless bird depended on him. And he was both amazed by and proud of how much Junior had grown in only a week—thanks to all the regular feedings.

"And I guess you'll be getting those wings soon," Jack said more quietly as he set Junior's eggs down in front of him. Jack watched the crow eat. Only recently, Junior had developed a habit of finishing his food and then hopping over to Jack and pecking his hand or arm lightly while looking up at him in a side-wise way. Jack was pretty sure it was Junior's way of saying "thank you." And Junior had also taken to hopping around the house and collecting small items—socks, spoons, bits of paper—and dropping them in a pile in the kitchen. This too, Jack knew, was Junior's way of showing his affection and appreciation.

After a couple of weeks, Jack began taking Junior outside. He'd let the growing bird hop around the backyard, feel the breeze, and hear the calls of other birds. Now and then, a group of crows would settle in the trees above Junior and watch him carefully. Often, the crows would fly down to the bottom branches and call to Junior. Junior would look up, ruffle his feathers, and call back with his awkward and questioning "caw?" Jack watched, knowing that one day this was the group of crows that Junior would probably fly away with. Already, Junior was beginning to flap his little wings anxiously when he'd see other birds flying overhead. It was only a matter of time.

Then one morning, with no warning whatsoever, Junior flapped clumsily across the kitchen while Jack was making eggs with raw peas. Junior took off from the edge of his box, made a huge racket of slapping and beating his wings, and finished with a crash landing in the sink. Immediately, he began casually preening his feathers in an attempt to look as though that was the exact flight pattern that he had intended. Jack laughed out loud.

"*Very* impressive. Quite a graceful landing, too, I must say." Jack smiled as he served Junior his breakfast in the kitchen sink. And though Jack was happy to see the young crow learning to fly, he was not looking forward to what he knew he'd have to do.

After breakfast, Jack carried Junior outside and set him on a low tree branch. Junior pecked Jack's shoulder affectionately as Jack took a long look at his crow. Then Jack left for work. He had never left Junior outside all day, but it would be the only way that the young bird would learn how to fly. Jack was well aware that he might never see Junior again. And as much as Jack hoped that the neighborhood flock of crows would come by and call for Junior to join them, Jack also secretly hoped that Junior would be waiting on the low branch.

That evening, Jack walked out to his backyard as soon as he got home. Junior was nowhere to be seen. Jack let out a whistle that he had been using to get Junior's attention, but the crow had clearly flown away. Then Jack heard a raucous caw from up above. He looked up just in time to see Junior hop off the roof, spread his wings, and wobble unsteadily through the air directly toward Jack's shoulder. Junior missed the shoulder by a mile and skidded into some bushes instead. Even so, Junior was obviously pleased with himself. He flapped awkwardly up to Jack's shoulder and perched there, cawing his achievement loudly and repeatedly into Jack's ear.

"Way to go, little guy," Jack said. Junior responded by nibbling at Jack's ear and grooming his hair.

For nearly three months, Junior hung around. Jack no longer allowed him in the house, so Junior quickly learned how to find his own food. Even so, he frequently rapped his beak loudly on the kitchen window and let out several annoyed caws when he smelled chicken being cooked. And, unlike a normal crow, Junior preferred sleeping on a lounge chair on the back patio as opposed to roosting in a tree or building a nest.

And Junior found many ways to entertain himself. He discovered that it was fun to chase the neighbor's dog and terrorize unsuspecting cats. It was even more fun to land on the hood of Jack's car when Jack was trying to pull it out of the driveway. No amount of honking and yelling could persuade Junior to budge. More often than not, Junior would stand proudly on the hood with his chest puffed out as Jack drove embarrassedly through the neighborhood. Only when Jack reached the main road would Junior fly back home.

But Junior's favorite game was collecting "presents" from around the neighborhood and depositing them at Jack's back door. Many times after a long day, Jack would return home to find a pile stacked with everything from plastic flowers to Barbie dolls. Once, Junior had even snatched a bra from a clothesline and placed it proudly on top of the pile. And while Jack was annoyed with having to find the owners of all the items (particularly the bra), he realized that, as with the kitchen piles, this was the crow's way of showing affection and gratitude.

Then one fall evening Junior was gone.

Jack whistled for Junior and searched the backyard. He looked to the roof and even at the hood of his car. But no Junior. *He's finally left with the neighborhood crows,* Jack thought sadly and happily at the same time. Jack had wondered why Junior had not already flown off. The local flock of crows often roosted nearby and raised an astounding symphony of caws. But Junior had never seemed particularly interested. However, this same flock migrated to a different part of the state during the winter. For all his hood riding and sleeping on lounge chairs, Junior's natural instinct had finally kicked in.

"Good luck, Junior," Jack said quietly, looking up at the darkening sky.

Many months later, as spring flowers were beginning to push up, Jack heard the crows return. He rushed out to his back yard and stared up into the branches of a neighbor's tree. Dozens of shiny black crows cawed, flapped, and chattered. Jack was certain that Junior was among the flock. Jack whistled and stood very still, but the crows simply continued their ruckus and then eventually flew off as a group. For weeks, Jack would step outside and whistle when he heard the crows in the neighboring trees. However, he never saw Junior again.

Or maybe he did.

On several occasions, Jack spotted a large crow sitting alone on the roof of his house. More than a few times, Jack noticed bird prints in the dust on the hood of his car. And nearly three years to the day after the bad storm that had blown Junior into Jack's kitchen, another strong storm came through. As the winds died down and the rain cleared, two crows settled outside on the kitchen windowsill. As Jack leaned close to the window to get a better look, the smaller of the two crows noticed him and flew away. But the bigger crow was not afraid. He stared right back at Jack for a long moment. Then the old crow ruffled his feathers, let out a raspy caw, and flew off to catch up with his mate.

A PRINCE

Preview

Centuries ago, greyhounds were treated like royalty. But picture a modern-day greyhound racetrack. Behind the track is a sickening sight: twenty starving greyhounds have been locked in a pen. Among them is "Trooper," a brave dog whose time is running out.

A PRINCE

A thousand years ago, a young king named "Howell the Good" sat by a creek that twisted through his land. Nearby, his horse rested and munched on grass, weary from a long day of hunting. Overhead, a late afternoon summer sun beat down, making the king sleepy. And surrounding the king were four greyhounds. The king's favorite greyhound, Argus, lay next to the king with his long, thin muzzle barely resting against the king's hand.

King Howell stroked Argus's head. Ever since the king could remember, greyhounds had lived in the castles of Europe. The elegant, sleek dogs were more than just hunting companions—they were respected and loved members of the royal families. They were the dogs of legends: Greek gods had owned them, Egyptian pharaohs had them wrapped as mummies and buried them in tombs, and they were the only dogs mentioned in the Bible. As the king's mind wandered through thousands of years of greyhounds, he grew sleepier and sleepier . . .

Wooooo! Wooooo! King Howell awoke with a jump at the sound of distant yelping and howling. How long had he slept? Only twilight glimmered on the horizon, and the first stars were twinkling. But there was still enough light to see the dreaded outline of the creeping visitors out in the field— wolves! In a panic, the king ran to his horse and called for his dogs. But the wolves were quickly moving closer. King Howell knew that as fast as his horse was, it would be no match for a pack of wolves. Still, he would have to try. One hungry wolf was dangerous to sheep and chickens. But a whole pack . . . The king turned to shout for his dogs again. Where *were* they?

Then the king saw something he had never

seen before. Argus was leading the three other greyhounds directly toward the wolves. They were moving slowly but deliberately.

"No! Argus, no!" King Howell shouted desperately. He also knew the greyhounds would not stand a chance in a fight with wolves. Greyhounds were built for speed, not battle. Their thin skin and delicate bones would be shredded and crushed like paper in the jaws of a wolf.

"Argus, come back!"

But Argus and the three other hounds did not even glance back at the king. The king watched in horror as the pack of ten or more wolves suddenly sprang forward and began running, low to the ground, toward the four dogs. King Howell felt as though he would be sick. He seemed to be frozen in some kind of terrifying nightmare where he would have to watch his old friend, his companion of ten years, get torn to pieces by wild animals. The king would not abandon Argus like that. He grabbed his sword and began to get off his horse.

But in a flash, the greyhounds suddenly darted to the left and sprinted across the open field. The wolves barked and snarled in anger and took off after them as fast as they could go. King Howell watched until the greyhounds and the wolves disappeared into the darkening woods. The high-pitched yaps of the pursuing wolves echoed distantly through the countryside.

The king dropped his sword as tears stung his eyes. He stood very still until the howling of the wolves grew silent. Then he slowly climbed back on his horse and rode by moonlight back to the castle alone.

Early the next morning, King Howell sat with his court in a large stone room near the castle gardens. A large door was open, and the smell of the garden blew through the room. The king was carefully re-reading a document he had written the night before.

"I don't think any one of you here would disagree with this new law," the king said quietly as he looked around the room. No one said a word.

"So then," the king continued, "from this day forward, the punishment for anyone who intentionally kills a greyhound will be death by hanging. It doesn't matter if it's a greyhound owned by a king or a common man. The punishment will be the same."

"But Sire, if you don't mind me asking, what prompted you to suddenly draw up this law?" an elderly duke asked.

Then the king smiled. He snapped his fingers three times and in ran Argus, his thin tail wagging quickly. Argus trotted over to the king and rested his head on the king's knee.

"Yesterday evening, my greyhounds saved

my life. They were not only brave; they were
also smart. I watched them change direction
so that the wolves would chase them and lose
interest in me. Of course, I knew right away
that the dogs would be fine. There isn't a wolf
alive that can outrun a greyhound."

The king played with Argus's ears for a
moment and then looked around the room
again.

"I feel that any animal that shows that kind
of devotion and love should be treated with
as much dignity and kindness as a human
being. These dogs should never, *never* be
treated cruelly or without respect."

All the men around the table smiled and
nodded.

"And so it shall be," the old duke concluded. "From this point on, the greyhound is
no less than a brother, a friend, a prince."

One thousand years later, a four-year-old
greyhound named "Trooper" sat huddled in a
hot, filthy cage in Arizona. He tried to rest, but
the heat and the noise from the racetrack kept
waking him up. Plus, it was nearly time for his
afternoon race. Trooper had been racing for
nearly three years, and he had a perfect sense,
within minutes, of when his owner would walk
in to take him to the track.

"Wake up, you worthless D-grade mutt!"
a rough voice bellowed in Trooper's direction.

Trooper's owner, a skinny little man named Dave, walked in smoking a cigarette and banged on the cage with a wrench.

"Your last chances are coming up," Dave continued in a threatening voice as if Trooper could understand him. "You keep running these races at a 'D' level, and it's curtains for you."

Trooper just cowered a little and wagged his tail weakly. His owner was not a kind man. He had never shown any affection to Trooper except for a couple of rough pats back when Trooper had won some races a year earlier. But Trooper, like most greyhounds, was a gentle and trusting animal. Although his owner mistreated him, Trooper felt a devotion to him that couldn't be helped.

"You stop makin' me money, you stop racing. You stop racing, you ain't worth anything. It's that simple," Dave muttered as he clamped on Trooper's muzzle and led him roughly through a smelly, dark tunnel that opened up to the racetrack. Trooper tugged hard on his leash as he heard the crowd. He got to race twice a day, and though the races only lasted about thirty seconds, that was his favorite minute of the day.

Trooper didn't know anything about D-grade racing. He didn't know that a year ago he had been an A-grade dog and had won his owner thousands of dollars. And he didn't know that if he didn't move up to at least a C-grade in the next couple of days, his favorite minute of the day would be gone forever.

"Now get out there and win me some money!" Dave shouted as he gave Trooper to the handler who walked him to the starting line. At the line were seven other greyhounds, all wearing the same leather muzzle and bright silk jackets that wrapped around their chests. All the dogs pawed anxiously, staring straight ahead down the track. Trooper stared, too. He was looking, watching, poised to explode as soon as . . .

And there it was! In a split second, all of the dogs burst forward in pursuit of a mechanical "rabbit" that always stayed just in front of them near the inside of the track. In less than two seconds, most of the dogs were running at nearly 40 miles an hour, a blur of dust and bright silk. Trooper did his best to catch the rabbit, too. But that same sharp pain in his left hind paw that he'd been feeling for weeks slowed him down again. By the time the dogs made the final turn, Trooper was in last place— again. But this time he trailed by more than twenty yards behind the seventh-place dog. Still, he wagged his tail and panted happily as he was returned to Dave.

"That does it!" Dave yelled as he yanked Trooper's leash savagely. "Forget about any more chances. I know a wasted, lazy dog when

I see one. Your time's up!"

Instead of walking Trooper back to his small metal cage, Dave walked him quickly to an area Trooper was not familiar with. Dave stood and talked briefly to a man Trooper had never seen before. Then Dave filled out a form, handed some money and Trooper's leash to the stranger, and turned to leave with not so much as a glance or a word to Trooper.

The stranger pulled Trooper roughly out to a fenced pen in the hot sun far away from the track and kennels. It was hidden by some low trees on one side and by an old storage building on the other. There were at least twenty other greyhounds in the fenced area—most of them were trying to cram into the narrow shaded area by the trees. The stranger snapped off Trooper's leash and gave him a little kick through the gate in the fence.

"Welcome to retirement," he said with a cruel laugh.

Three days later, Trooper sat sadly in the corner of the pen. He could hear the distant roar of the crowd watching the races every morning and afternoon—why didn't his master come and take him in to race? What was wrong? The other dogs in the pen were not particularly friendly. Nearly all of them were older than Trooper, and most of them were limping or licking sores and cuts. A few barely moved at all.

Every morning, the stranger brought some buckets of lukewarm water and bowls of tough, nearly rotten meat for the dogs. As unappealing as the food was, the dogs growled and snarled at one another as they ate. There was never enough to go around, and all of the dogs were extremely hungry. The outlines of ribs and leg bones were clearly visible, and a few dogs were too weak to even stumble to the bowls. Trooper watched in fear as some of the dogs who hadn't moved in a couple of days were dragged out by their legs and tossed in the back of a rusty pickup truck.

Nine days later, Trooper could not put any weight on his sore left hind paw. It had gotten worse every day since he had been brought to the pen. And now it slowed him down as he struggled to the food bowls in the morning. By the time he reached the bowls, nearly all of the meat had disappeared, and Trooper had to settle for gristle and bone. Before long, Trooper's ribs began poking out, and sores began showing up on his sides from lying in the dirt most of the day. Trooper no longer pricked up his ears when he heard the crowd in the distance. Only in his dreams late at night would vague memories of chasing the rabbit come back to him, and he would twitch his thin legs in his sleep and whine quietly.

One morning, Trooper gazed through half-shut, bloodshot eyes at two people, a man and a woman, standing by the fence. They were staring at the dogs with horrified expressions. Every few seconds, the woman would take some pictures, and the man would write something in a notebook. Suddenly, the stranger came rushing over.

"What the hell do you think you're doing?" he yelled at the woman taking the pictures. "Get away from my dogs."

"Your dogs?" the man asked, his voice shaking with anger. "You actually have the nerve to admit that these are *your* dogs?"

The stranger looked confused for a moment. Then he looked a little frightened. "Now look, I don't want any trouble. These are just old track dogs that can't run anymore. I do my best to take care of them in their . . . uh . . . old age."

"If this is your 'best,'" the woman said evenly, "then I would hate to see your worst. Most of these dogs are injured or sick. All of them are starving."

The stranger opened his mouth to protest, but the man handed him an official-looking document and held up a badge.

"You're going to need to come with us," was all he said.

"It's okay, buddy. It's okay."

Trooper drifted in and out of consciousness, vaguely aware that someone was petting his head and stroking his back. Something softer than he'd ever felt was underneath him, and a cool breeze seemed to be blowing. A young man with a quiet voice was sitting next to Trooper and watching him closely as he petted him.

"They got you just in time, didn't they?" he said gently.

Then another voice appeared.

"Daddy, when can he chase a ball?"

The strange, little voice made Trooper lift his head and look. He had never seen such a small human—children had not been allowed at the track. He looked at the child briefly, barely wagged his tail, and put his head back down with a sigh.

"As soon as his paw is healed and he gets a little stronger, Erin," the man said to his daughter.

"Tomorrow?" the little girl asked hopefully.

"No. Maybe in a few weeks. You'll have to be patient, sweetie. He's had a rough time."

Erin reached over and touched Trooper's bandaged paw very carefully. He opened his eyes half-mast and gazed at her.

The father smiled to himself. Two weeks earlier he had read an article in the paper about a local organization called the Greyhound

Rescue Group. This group worked hard to make sure that racing greyhounds were not being abused or mistreated at the local tracks. Some greyhound owners took good care of their dogs and loved them, but far too many saw the dogs as nothing more than money-makers that could be thrown away when they stopped winning.

The article had gone on to explain that a member of the organization, along with an Animal Control officer, had discovered the starving dogs in the pen behind the track. The owner had been arrested, and the dogs were immediately taken to an animal hospital. Sadly, eight dogs were so starved and sick that they had to be put to sleep. But the twelve other dogs, including Trooper, were treated and put up for adoption.

The father did not remember the true story about "Howell the Good" that he had read to his daughter several months earlier. So he was not sure why Erin often mentioned wanting a greyhound. And he was surprised that, when he explained what had happened to Trooper, his eight-year-old daughter had asked, "Will they kill the owner?" And now he wondered about one more thing.

"Prince," Erin whispered as she leaned over near Trooper's ear.

"'Prince'?" the father asked. "But, Erin, his

name is Trooper."

Erin made a funny face. "Daddy, we can't call him that. That's a dog's name."

"Well, sweetie, he *is* a dog."

Erin didn't say anything, but she had a secretive sort of smile on her face as she stroked Trooper's head.

"A brother, a friend . . ." Erin seemed to be saying mostly to herself. Then she looked up at her father with a big grin. She reached down and put her arms around her new dog and said with a nod, "A Prince."

THE ORPHAN WHALES

Preview

One night, thirty whales swim ashore and become trapped on a beach. Within hours, people swarm the beach, struggling to push the four-ton animals back into the sea. Suddenly, the saddest sight— three baby whales gasping for air. How can they be saved?

THE ORPHAN WHALES

One night, as a full moon crept through the sky, something very strange began happening in the ocean near Cape Cod, Massachusetts. A large group of whales was swimming straight toward the beach. As they got closer and closer, some of the biggest whales, weighing nearly four tons, began to get stuck in the sand. Behind the big whales came the smaller whales, and behind the smaller whales came the babies. When daybreak finally came, a horrible sight met the eyes of the first people out on the beach—thirty whales lay gasping and motionless along the sand. Many of them were sending out high-pitched distress signals. A few were already dead.

"Cover them in wet towels! Pour water on them!"

"No! Push them back out to sea!"

"Turn them over so they can breathe!"

Within a couple of hours, dozens of people swarmed the beach, desperately trying to do something, *anything*, to help the stranded animals. The tide had gone out, leaving the whales on the dry beach. It would be another eight hours until the tide rolled back in. And though whales are mammals, not fish, they still needed to keep their skin wet to stay alive. Many people brought buckets and made trip after trip to the ocean, bringing water back to the whales and pouring it over them.

Meanwhile, a van full of people from the New England Aquarium was rushing up from Boston to help. Veterinarians, volunteers, divers, and scientists from the aquarium all sat quietly during the two-hour drive. In charge was Greg Early. He had seen stranded whales before, and he knew how hard it was going to be.

"We'll be a little like doctors walking through a disaster zone," Greg explained to the nervous group. "Bodies will be everywhere, and we'll have to make some hard decisions about which whales might survive and which are beyond help."

"But why did the whales swim ashore in the first place?" one of the divers asked.

Greg shook his head. "No one knows why whales do this. It's been happening for centuries, but we're still no closer to understanding why."

"But then," the diver asked, "shouldn't we maybe just leave them alone? Maybe it's natural."

Before Greg could respond, a volunteer quietly said, "You may be right. But it doesn't seem natural to the human spirit to just sit by and watch so many majestic creatures suffer and die."

By afternoon, however, the spirits of nearly everyone on the beach were sinking very low. As hard as the volunteers and divers tried, they were unable to get any of the whales back into open water. The vets examined whale after whale whose own body weight was crushing it to death. Without the weightlessness of water to swim in, the whales were literally caving in. And though Greg had witnessed this same kind of horror before, it didn't make it any easier. It looked as though every one of the thirty whales might die; it all seemed so hopeless and so unfair.

Then some excited yelling came from further down the beach. Several people were waving their hands at Greg.

"Quick! We've got calves. Still alive!"

Greg went running down the beach. "Calves" were baby whales, and their chances of survival, since they were so much smaller, were actually greater. Greg rushed over to where the small crowd was gathered. Lying not too far apart were three tiny ("tiny" being eight feet long) whales. All three were still moving but very weak. Greg knew their time was running out.

"We've got three orphans here," Greg said, thinking out loud. "They're too young to try and put back in the water. Their only chance for survival is a rescue mission . . ."

Within two hours, all three whales had been carefully lifted and placed in a large truck for the trip to the New England Aquarium in Boston. During the ride, the whales were surrounded by volunteers who continuously squeezed water over them with giant sponges. Some of the volunteers even sang quietly to the babies to try and keep them calm. And bags of ice were scattered across the calves' shiny black backs.

"Baby whales are like car radiators," Greg had explained. "When they get upset, they can run really hot."

On the way to the aquarium, the volunteers named the three calves. The largest was named "Notch" because he had a nick in his top fin. The next smallest was named "Tag" because he had been given a yellow tag on the beach to identify him as a whale to save. The smallest was named "Baby" because he was, after all, the baby. As the truck pulled into the aquarium, a vet called in from the beach back at Cape Cod.

"Take good care of those orphan whales," he said. "They're the only survivors. The last whale out here just died."

Around the country, all eyes were now on the three survivors. Never before had three baby whales been rescued and taken into captivity. The plan was to nurse them back to health and then release them back into the ocean. From California to Massachusetts, everyone was rooting for the orphans and wishing them a speedy recovery. However, Notch, Tag, and Baby were not very happy during their first days in their new home—a 60,000-gallon holding pool at the aquarium. Notch wasn't breathing well, Tag panicked and kept swimming into the walls, and Baby refused to eat. After a couple more days, Notch and Tag were adjusting better, but Baby was still not eating.

"He's still too young for solid food," the vet observed.

The vet and his team decided to put a tube down Baby's throat so that food could be pumped directly into his stomach. Baby did his best to whack the vet with his flippers, splash water, and clench his teeth so that the tube could not be put down his throat. He even sucked in water and then blew it in everyone's faces. But, finally, the tube was in place, and Baby's stomach was filled with herring and vitamins. Once Baby was fed, his natural desire to keep eating kicked in. Before long, he was eating whole fish just like the two bigger whales.

As the weeks went by, the three calves became very close to one another. Whales, by nature, are very social animals—they like to hang out in large groups, called "pods," and play together. Notch, Tag, and Baby had only their very small pod of three, but they invented all kinds of games to keep them entertained. Like children, they liked to play with their food. A favorite game involved balancing fish on top of their heads or swimming upside down while balancing fish on their stomachs. Whether or not they were playing a game, the three whales always stayed close together. Even when they slept, their fins or tails touched one another's.

Greg and the staff at the aquarium watched the progress of the whales with mixed emotions. They were thrilled to see that the young whales were learning to stick together as a group. In the wild, whales stuck together for more than just fun and games—being in a large pod protected them from shark attacks. But

Notch, Tag, and Baby were not a big enough group. Their release time was growing nearer and nearer, but how would they survive?

"These three will be shark bait," Greg said with a worried frown as he and several of his staff watched the whales chase each other around the tank.

"I hope not," one of the vets replied sadly. "Plus, the whole world will be watching their release."

"Would it be possible," a young marine scientist slowly asked, "to find a pod and release these three close to it and hope for the best?"

Greg and the staff sat down and discussed this idea for most of the afternoon. Finally, they put a plan together that involved a scientific research ship and a helicopter.

"In two weeks, then, we will take the three whales out to sea on the ship," Greg said. "Meanwhile, the helicopter will fly nearby, looking for a pod. When one is spotted, we'll catch up with it and release Notch, Tag, and Baby."

"But how will we know for sure if the three join the pod and survive?" one of the staff asked. "I wish there were a way to give Notch a call once a week and ask him how they're all doing."

This made everyone laugh, but it also made everyone think.

"You know," one of the scientists said, "we could easily clip transmitters on their back fins. Whenever the whales come to the surface for air, the transmitter will send signals to a special radio that will indicate where they are. The batteries last about three months. If we keep getting beeps, we'll know they're all right."

Two weeks later, Greg stood on the deck of the *Albatross IV*, a 180-foot research ship. Not far away, a helicopter was hovering above a huge pod of whales. Greg nervously paced the deck, stopping every now and then to look in on the three whales. Each one had been carefully "packed" into a wet sheepskin-lined container. Volunteers had covered them in ice and saltwater. And each whale sported a zinc oxide mask to protect him from the sun during the trip out to sea. They looked like a cross between a lifeguard and a clown. Greg had to smile in spite of his nervousness. Baby glanced up at him with her small dark eyes and white zinc mask as if to say, *What now?*

The ship grew closer and closer to the pod as the crew began to prepare the whales for release. The plan was to release the whales, one at a time, into an underwater rope cage (nicknamed the "whale jail") to let them get used to the water and their new surroundings for an hour or so. Then all three would be released into the ocean at the same time. But things did not go as planned.

"Cut the ropes! Cut the ropes!" The frantic voices of the crew shouted down to the divers who were positioned around the whale jail. Notch, the first whale lowered into the rope cage, had not calmly swum around as expected. He had immediately lunged into the cage's rope side and had tangled himself up in rope. This was deadly dangerous. Since whales must surface and breathe air every ten to fifteen minutes, Notch would drown if the divers could not cut him free quickly.

"Watch out for his tail!" (One of the divers had once had a leg broken by a wild, flapping whale tail.)

"Careful with the knives!" (In their hurry to cut the cage open, the divers' knives drew dangerously close to Notch's face.)

"There goes his transmitter!" (And in Notch's struggle, his radio transmitter popped off and fell to the bottom of the ocean.)

But finally Notch was free. The crew was disappointed that the "whale jail" had not worked. But more troublesome was the fact that Notch was out there on his own. Without his two companions, Notch would be confused and frightened, and he might not approach the nearby large pod of whales. But there was no time to waste with worrying about what might happen.

Quickly, Tag and Baby were lowered into the ocean at the same time. The cage was no longer there to be a safe place to grow used to their new world, but unlike Notch, the two young whales swam carefully near the ship for a while before slowly heading out to sea. Greg and the crew cheered, hugged, and even cried as they watched Tag and Baby swim away to freedom, side by side.

But before the two were more than twenty yards away, Greg saw something that brought a wide smile to his face. Heading toward the ship was a whale—with a zinc oxide mask. It was Notch returning for his friends. Notch met up with Tag and Baby, and all three continued together in the direction of the large pod.

"True friendship if I ever saw it," Greg said to himself quietly.

Beep! Beep! Beep!

Kathy Krieger, a scientist at the New England Aquarium, was flying in a small plane just above the ocean near Cape Cod. It was a few weeks after the three whales had been released, and suddenly her locator radio began to beep. It was a beautifully clear summer day, so Kathy looked down to the water. There, she saw a wonderful sight. Two large pods of whales were meeting up with one another, and right in the middle of it all, Kathy could see the glint of the sun off of two radio transmitters— Baby and Tag! *And I know Notch must be right there with them*, Kathy thought as she radioed the news back to Greg.

For more than three months, Baby and Tag's radios continued to beep from time to time. As a result, scientists at the aquarium were able to follow the movement of the pod and learn a great deal about how and where whales live, how deep they dive for fish, and where they go to rest. Finally, the batteries on the transmitters died, and the story of Notch, Baby, and Tag came to a close. But they would never be forgotten.

"We gave Baby, Tag, and Notch a wonderful gift," Greg Early commented to a friend one evening as they sat staring out to the ocean's horizon. "We gave them a safe return to the sea."

Greg paused and thought about all that was learned by studying the three whales and then tracking them. But, more importantly, he thought about how, from coast to coast, it had touched the human spirit to rescue, save, and then release such amazing creatures.

"But, of course," Greg said, "they gave us a gift that was just as wonderful."